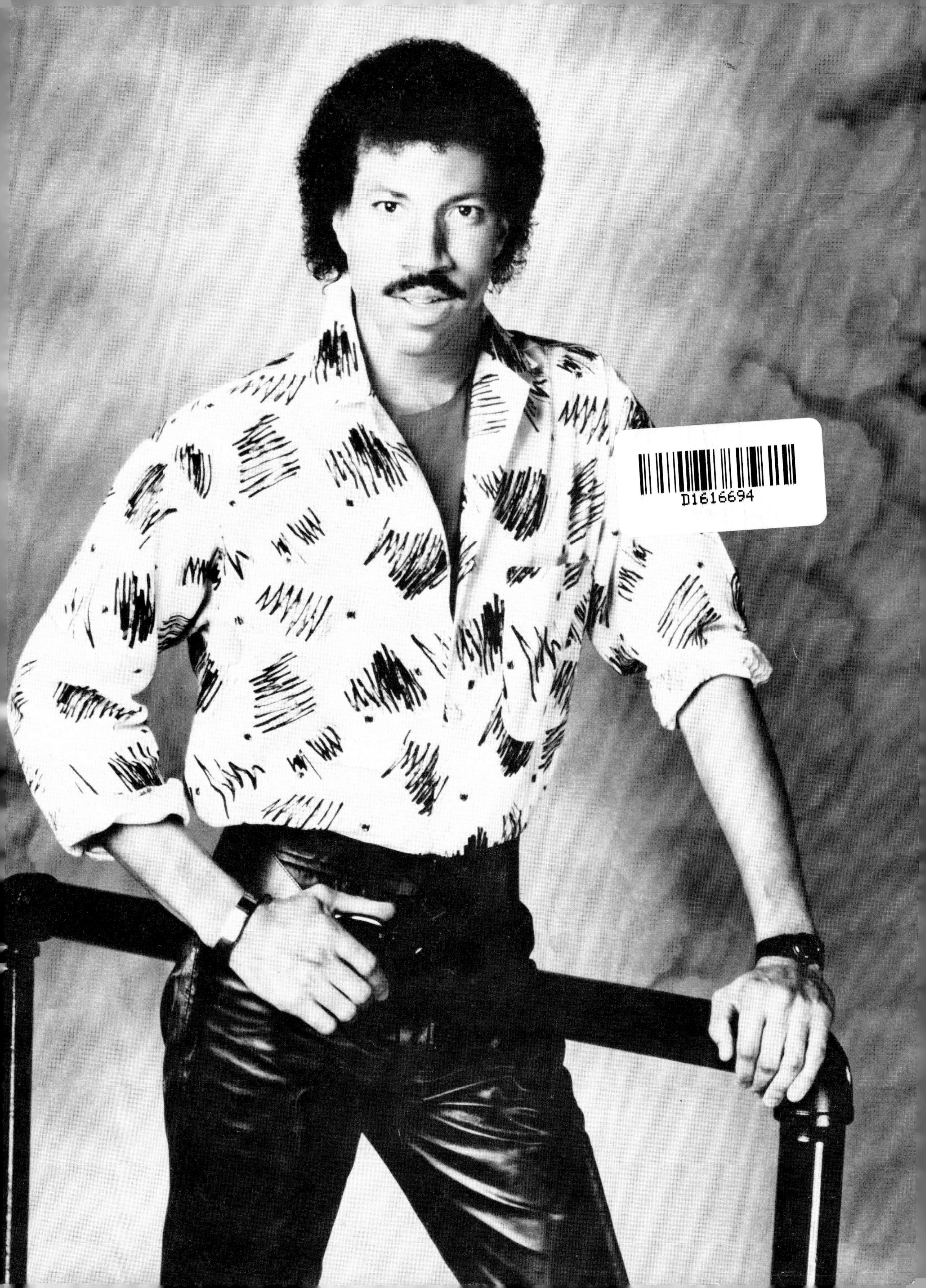

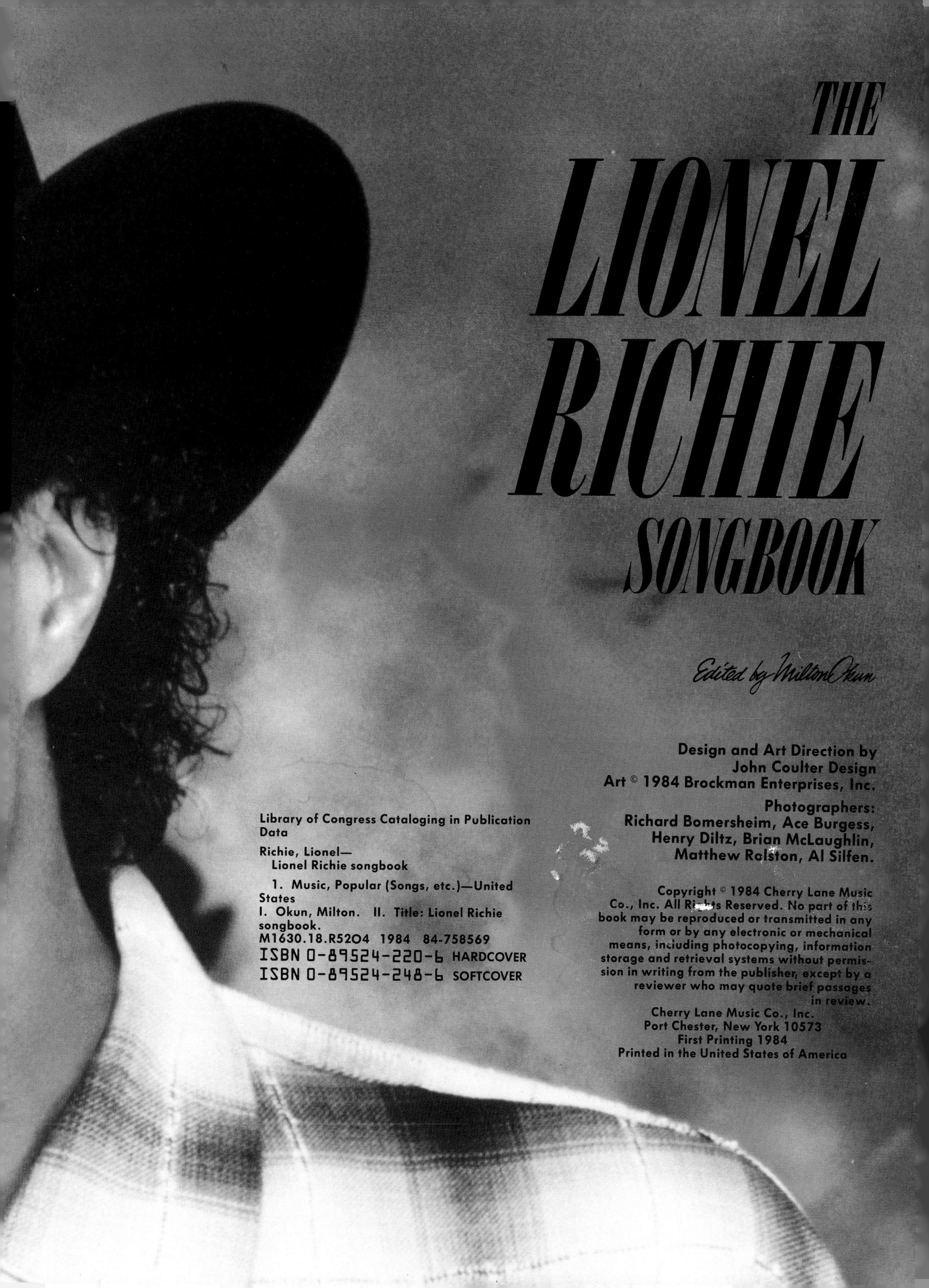

THE LIONEL RICHIE SONGBOOK

Edited by Milton Okun

Design and Art Direction by
John Coulter Design
Art © 1984 Brockman Enterprises, Inc.

Photographers:
Richard Bomersheim, Ace Burgess,
Henry Diltz, Brian McLaughlin,
Matthew Ralston, Al Silfen.

Library of Congress Cataloging in Publication Data

Richie, Lionel—
Lionel Richie songbook

1. Music, Popular (Songs, etc.)—United States
I. Okun, Milton. II. Title: Lionel Richie songbook.
M1630.18.R5204 1984 84-758569
ISBN 0-89524-220-6 HARDCOVER
ISBN 0-89524-248-6 SOFTCOVER

Cherry Lane Music Co., Inc.
Port Chester, New York 10573
First Printing 1984
Printed in the United States of America

CONTENTS

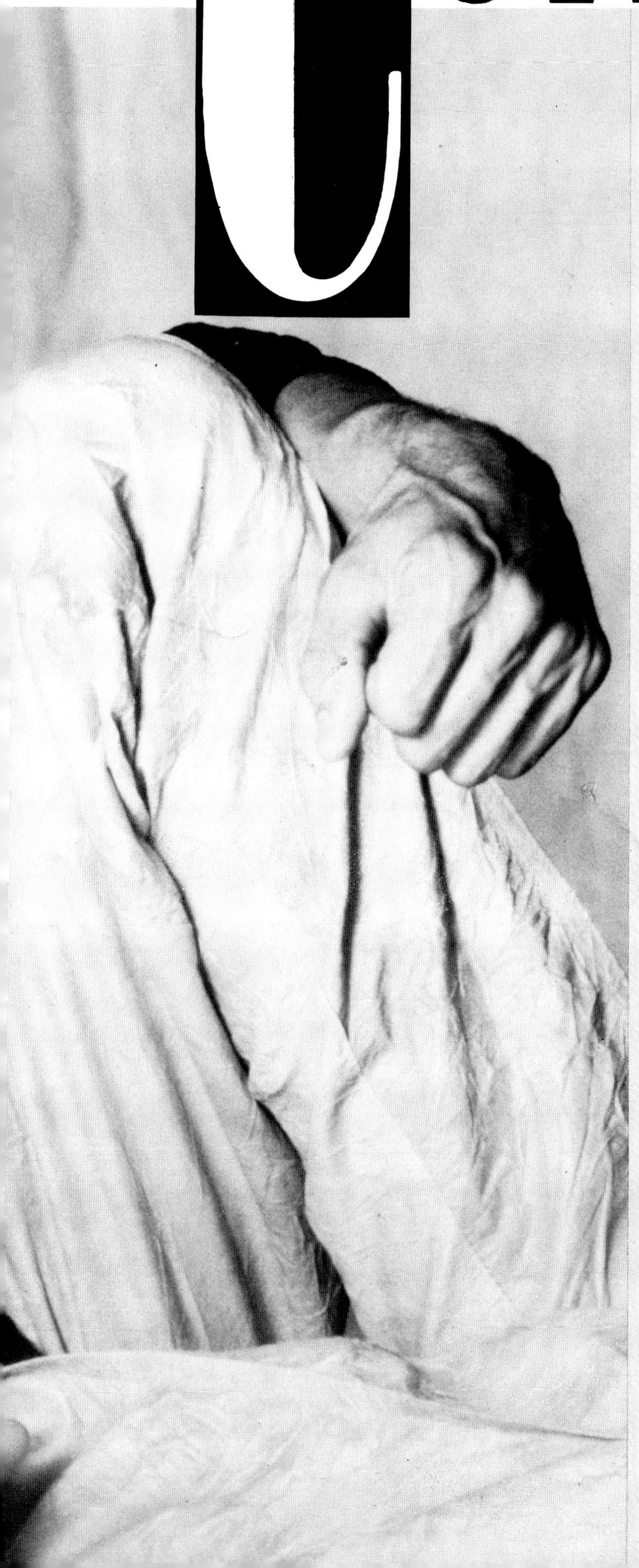

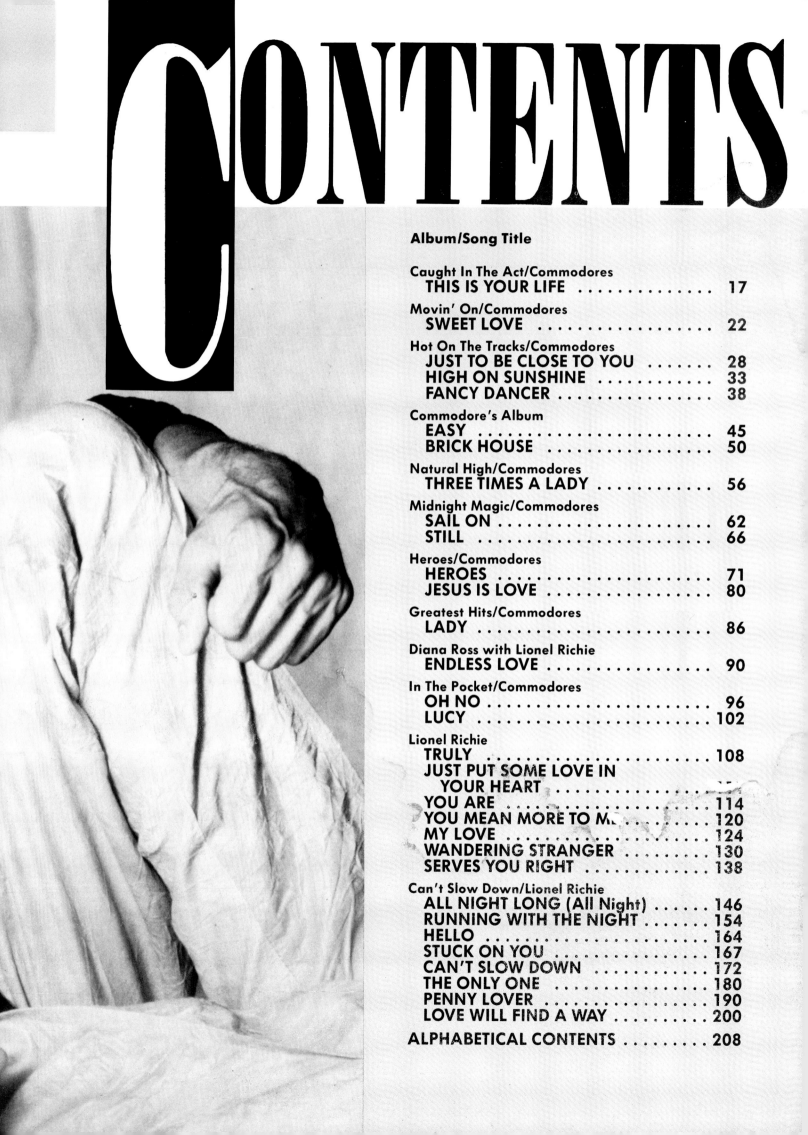

Album/Song Title

Lionel in "Running with the Night" video.

A BRIEF HISTORY

The most popular composer of his generation, Lionel Richie's achievements have certainly been awesome; yet, Richie prefers to see himself as only on the way to realizing all of his potential as a songwriter.

"Success gives freedom," he says, "freedom to try new things. Freedom to go in new directions. There's no end to what I can create, no end to what I can write. Everything is about sounds now. Elvis Presley and Bill Haley & the Comets did their recordings with upright bass. In the sixties the groups had electric basses and guitars. Now it's synthesizers, synthesized drums, synthesized bass—computer-this, computer-that. It's amazing. The music is the same; it's still all about having a song. It's just that the technology allows you to do more things than ever before. You used to need forty musicians to have a string section. Now all you need is your ten fingers. You can create an evening under the stars with the touch of your fingers. What's happening to me musically is that I'm discovering sounds, wonderful sounds created on wonderful electronic instruments.

"But I never want to go too fast and leave any of my fans behind," he adds, with a sincerity that typifies his down-to-earth approach to life. "The whole point is to take people with me."

Since the inception of his performing career with the Commodores in the early seventies, Lionel Richie has taken audiences of all ages, all colors and all musical tastes on a unique and melodic journey with his soulful, flowing balladeering. It is a journey that encompasses pop, country music, rhythm 'n' blues and reggae, drawing on his Alabama roots, as imbued with history and music as the house he grew up in with his grandparents in Tuskegee. Once owned by Booker T. Washington, founder of Richie's alma mater, Tuskegee Institute (where he first met the other Commodores), the house was filled with the music of Bach and Beethoven as played by Richie's grandmother, a piano instructor. To the classics, young Richie added his own mix of R&B and country influences to produce the blend that would eventually come to be thought of as the music of a natural homespun genius.

Lionel Richie would not concur with that high-toned evaluation of his work. "I would love to say I went to Juilliard and that someone discovered me writing music," he says, "but that's not the way it happened. Everything just evolved from the fact that early on in life I found I was too small to play football, too short to play basketball and too slow to run track." While his own explanation may be overly modest, even evasive, it's also indicative of the humor with which he views himself and his career.

"I don't know this guy Lionel Richie," he says. "To be honest, he's kind of a fascination with me, as if there's someone else using my name. They say all these things about me, but as far as I'm concerned, I'm still the guy I always was. I was not a lady's man, and the crowd I hung out with was not the in-crowd. My sport was tennis, which, in the sixties, was not exactly the most masculine sport in the world. So when people get all excited about me now, I start laughing and hope this other guy they're all talking about hurries and shows up."

"Identity problems" aside, Richie's winning combination of modesty, wit and sincerity is coupled with a professionalism unmatched in show business. It was at Motown Records in the mid- seventies that he and the Commodores received a virtual masters degree in entertainment, from stage presence through choreogra-

CONTINUED▶

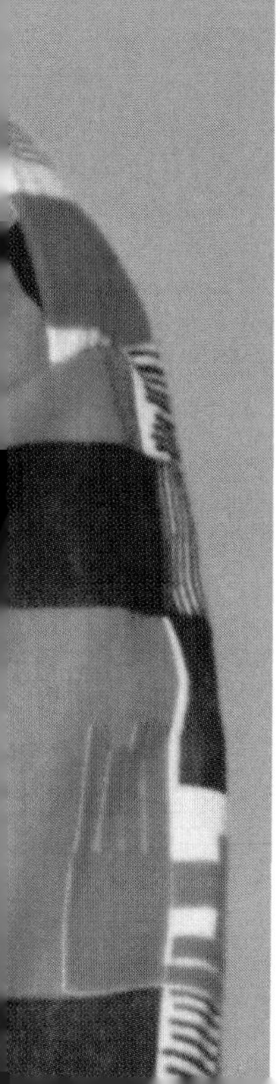

phy. Richie himself benefitted from tutorials at the feet of such songwriting masters as Holland-Dozier-Holland (Eddie-Lamont-Brian, who wrote many of Motown's greatest hits for the Supremes, the Four Tops, the Marvelettes, et.al.) and Norman Whitfield (producer of the Temptations). His musical "guidance counselor" was Berry Gordy, Jr., Motown's founder. Obviously the Commodores were *A* students, even before Lionel Richie stepped to the head of the class; a class act even before Richie graduated, numbering among their achievements such stellar tunes as *Sweet Love*, *Brick House*, and *Just to be Close to You*. Their biggest hits, *Easy* from 1977, *Three Times a Lady*, from 1978 *Sail On* and *Still* from 1980, finally established Richie as a songwriter of the first rank, causing industry heads to turn.

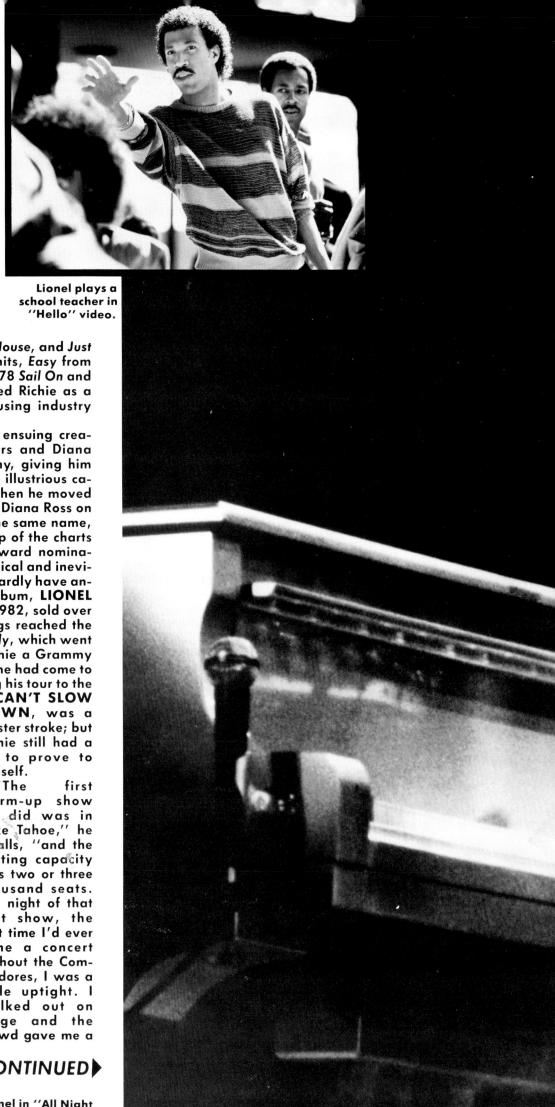

Lionel plays a school teacher in "Hello" video.

The chief recipients of Richie's ensuing creative largesse were Kenny Rogers and Diana Ross. Richie wrote *Lady* for Kenny, giving him the biggest single of his long and illustrious career—six weeks at number one. Then he moved onto another plane, dueting with Diana Ross on *Endless Love*, from the movie of the same name, which spent nine weeks at the top of the charts and earned him an Academy Award nomination. A solo career seemed the logical and inevitable next step, but Richie could hardly have anticipated its extent. His debut album, **LIONEL RICHIE**, released in September, 1982, sold over 4 million copies. Three of its songs reached the top five: *You Are*, *My Love* and *Truly*, which went to number one and garnered Richie a Grammy for Best Pop Male Vocalist. The time had come to take the show on the road. Timing his tour to the release of his second album, **CAN'T SLOW DOWN**, was a master stroke; but Richie still had a lot to prove to himself.

"The first warm-up show we did was in Lake Tahoe," he recalls, "and the seating capacity was two or three thousand seats. The night of that first show, the first time I'd ever done a concert without the Commodores, I was a little uptight. I walked out on stage and the crowd gave me a

CONTINUED

Lionel in "All Night Long" video.

standing ovation. I couldn't believe it. I felt like I was home. Then, the first real big date of the tour was in Toledo, Ohio. It was sold out, and again, for the opening song, it was pandemonium. The first five or six shows I did were very emotional experiences for me. It was wonderful to go after a dream and have that dream come alive right in front of me.''

It should be said that Richie, for his part, aids immeasurably in nudging that dream toward reality by providing his audience, whether on a college campus, or in the vast reaches of New York's Radio City Music Hall, or packed at tables in the steamy lounges of Las Vegas, with an absolutely spectacular show, complete with smoke bombs, fireworks, break dancers and the incomparable Richie charisma. It is Lionel Richie's singular talent, as more than one reviewer has pointed out, that he can make a stage ''flap with percussive and rhythmic waves. The total thrust is high energy fun.'' At the same time, he can hold an audience captive merely with his voice, that famous style dubbed ''vocaressing'' for its powers of intimacy and truth, speaking to all as if it were speaking to one.

And if the audiences were dancing in the aisles at his sold-out performances, they were dancing in the aisles the day after, at the record malls of the nation, where they bought his new album in record numbers, making **CAN'T SLOW DOWN** the largest selling album in Motown history and lifting the singles *All Night Long, Running with the Night, Hello* and *Stuck On You* to the upper reaches of the charts.

As if it weren't apparent, performing live for Richie is still a blast. ''Touring is recess,'' he says. ''It's just the best. I love being out there.'' And yet, what would a Lionel Richie show be without Lionel Richie's songs?

''Being in the studio recording is very hard work,'' he says. ''It's so serious and intense and lasts for so long. It requires so much mental energy to come up with each song, and I am so critical of everything. I still come from the standpoint that a song must first pass the test of the ''hum.'' No music, no drums, no synthesizers, just me humming. A great song is one that you can just hum. I try to get my songs to pass the melody test. Then I add words. If you've got the melody and the words, then you can add anything—guitars, drums, even visuals.''

Not to be regarded lightly in this day and age, the video realm is another in which Richie has already left an impressive mark. Directed by Bob Rafelson, the ''All Night Long'' video was one of 1983's best. ''Everyone saw a party, a celebration, with all sorts of people, and that's what the song was all about. It was the best thing in the world.'' But if this successful foray onto the TV screen portends a future on the network side of that medium, Richie isn't letting on. ''It's an interesting option,'' is all he will allow. ''Time will tell.''

Surely, he will take whatever new reaches his career may cover with the same easygoing stride and sense of natural humor as he's done in the past. ''My mom was telling me that people ask her how it feels to have Lionel Richie as a son,'' he laughs, ''and she says to them, 'I don't feel anything. That's just Lionel, Jr.!'''

As these 31 songs bear out, Mom's ''Jr.'' is a grown up composer now. Let us all delight in his maturity.

FACT SHEET

—He's had a number one single six years in a row.

—He won a Grammy in 1983 for Best Pop Male Vocal Performance on his number one smash, *Truly.*

—He's been nominated 18 times for various Grammy Awards, including five nominations in 1983 for the most successful single of his career, *All Night Long.*

—*All Night Long*, the Gold single from his current solo album, was number one for four weeks.

—*CAN'T SLOW DOWN* is the biggest-selling album in the history of Motown Records. His first solo Lp, *LIONEL RICHIE*, is the third biggest.

—Together his two solo albums have sold over seven million copies.

—He released 11 albums with The Commodores beginning in 1974: three are Platinum (over 1 million sold) and four are Gold (500,000 sold).

—He won Best Song for The People's Choice Awards (determined by Gallup poll) *five years in a row*, beginning in 1979 with *Three Times a Lady.*

—*Endless Love*, the movie theme song he wrote and produced, and sang with Diana Ross, was number one for *nine weeks* and was nominated for an Academy Award.

—He wrote Kenny Rogers' first number one pop single, *Lady*, at Rogers' request.

—*Lady* was the only new song included on *KENNY ROGERS' GREATEST HITS* in 1980. The Lp has sold over 15 million copies worldwide.

—He produced Rogers' 3 million-selling *SHARE YOUR LOVE* Lp in 1981.

—He won the Grand Prize as Best Artist at the 1983 Tokyo Music Festival.

—He completed his first solo tour in January 1984: 80 concerts across the United States including sold-out weeks at both Radio City Music Hall in New York and The Universal Amphitheatre in Los Angeles. The second tour (summer/fall 1984) covered 50 venues in the U.S. and Canada and played to sold-out crowds.

—He toured Japan on his own for the first time in 1983 and sold out every show.

—*All Night Long* won an American Music Award as Best Soul Single (1984).

—He was the first solo host of The American Music Awards in 1984 and the telecast won the highest ratings of any music awards show ever.

—He was asked by Dick Clark and ABC-TV to repeat as solo host in 1985.

—The Detroit *News* called his concert " . . . hands down the finest live pop music achievements any of us will experience this year."

—He was honored as The United Negro College Fund's Alumnus of the Year in March, 1984.

—He supports SHARE, The American Cancer Society, The Juvenile Diabetes Association, and is foster father of six.

—His videos are in heavy rotation on MTV and all other major music video shows.

—He performed *All Night Long* at the Gala Olympic Closing Ceremonies before an estimated live and television audience of 3 billion.

—The video of *Hello* brought him kudos for his dramatic skills.

—*Hello* was number 1 on the charts for two weeks and in the top 10 for eight weeks.

AWARDS & NOMINATIONS

1977 Grammy Nominations: Best Rhythm & Blues Song, *Brick House*/The Commodores; Best Rhythm & Blues Song, *Easy*/The Commodores; Best Rhythm & Blues Vocal Performance by a Duo or Group, *Easy*/The Commodores.

1978 Grammy Nominations: Song of the Year, *Three Times a Lady*/Composer; Best Pop Vocal Performance by a Duo or Group, *Three Times a Lady*/The Commodores; Best Rhythm & Blues Vocal Performance by a Duo or Group, *Natural High*/The Commodores.

1979 American Music Award: Most Popular Single, *Three Times a Lady*/The Commodores.
People's Choice Award: Best Song, *Three Times a Lady*/The Commodores.
Grammy Nominations: Best Pop Vocal Performance by a Duo or Group, *Sail On*/The Commodores; Best Rhythm & Blues Vocal Performance by a Duo or Group, *Midnight Magic*/The Commodores.

1980 American Music Award: Favorite Soul Group, The Commodores.
People's Choice Award: Best Song, *Still*/The Commodores.
Grammy Nominations: Record of the Year, *Lady*/Producer; Song of the Year, *Lady*/Composer; Best Rhythm & Blues Performance by a Duo or Group, *Heroes*/The Commodores; Best Inspirational Performance by a Duo or Group, *Jesus Is Love*/The Commodores.

1981 People's Choice Award: Best Song, *Lady*/Composer (Performed by Kenny Rogers)
National Association of Record Merchandisers: Best Selling Single, *Endless Love*/Composer/Producer (Performed with Diana Ross).
Grammy Nominations: Record of the Year, *Endless Love*; Song of the Year, *Endless Love*/Composer; Producer of the Year; Best Album or Original Score Written for Motion Picture or Television Special, *Endless Love*/with Thomas McClary and Jonathan Tunick; Best Performance by a Duo or Group with Vocal, *Endless Love*/with Diana Ross; Best Rhythm & Blues Vocal Performance by a Duo or Group, *Lady You Bring Me Up*/The Commodores.

1982 Grammy Award: Best Pop Male Vocal Performance, *Truly*.
Academy Award Nomination: Best Song, *Endless Love*.
American Music Awards: Best Soul Single, *Endless Love*; Best Pop Single, *Endless Love*.
People's Choice Award: Best Song, *Endless Love*.

1983 American Music Awards: Best Pop Single, *Truly*; Best Soul Male Vocalist.
People's Choice Award: Best Song, *Truly*.
Tokyo Music Festival: Grand Prize.
Grammy Nominations: Producer of the Year; Record of the Year, *All Night Long*;* Song of the Year, *All Night Long**; Best Pop Male Vocal Performance, *All Night Long**; Best Instrumental Arrangement Behind a Vocal, *All Night Long*.*
NAACP Image Award: Best Male Artist.

1984 American Music Award: Best Soul Single, *All Night Long*.
United Negro College Fund: Alumnus of the Year.
Children's Diabetes Foundation: Man of the Year.
ASCAP: Writer of the Year.
NMPA Award: Best Soul Single, *All Night Long*.

* Only the single *All Night Long* qualified for 1983 Grammy consideration. The album on which it appears, *CAN'T SLOW DOWN*, was released six weeks after the single and will qualify for the 1984 awards.

DISCOGRAPHY

Release Date	Record Label	Artist	LP Title	Cert. (G/P)	Single	Cert. (G/P)
1974	Motown	Commodores	MACHINE GUN		*Machine Gun*	Gold
1975	Motown	Commodores	CAUGHT IN THE ACT		*Slippery When Wet* *This Is Your Life*	
1975	Motown	Commodores	MOVIN' ON		*Sweet Love*	
1976	Motown	Commodores	HOT ON THE TRACKS		*Just To Be Close To You*	
1977	Motown	Commodores	COMMODORES	Platinum	*Easy* *Brick House*	Gold Gold
1977	Motown	Commodores	COMMODORES LIVE	Gold	*Too Hot To Trot*	
1978	Motown	Commodores	COMMODORES GREATEST HITS	Gold		
1978	Motown	Commodores	NATURAL HIGH	Gold	*Three Times A Lady*	Plat.
1979	Motown	Commodores	MIDNIGHT MAGIC	Plat.	*Sail On* *Still*	Gold Gold
1980	Motown	Commodores	HEROES	Gold	*Old Fashioned Love* *Heroes*	
1981	Motown	Commodores	IN THE POCKET	Plat.	*Lady You Bring Me Up* *Oh No* *Why You Wanna Try Me*	Gold
1981	Polygram	Lionel Richie with Diana Ross	ENDLESS LOVE SOUNDTRACK*		*Endless Love*	Gold
1982	Motown	Lionel Richie	LIONEL RICHIE	Plat.	*Truly* *You Are* *My Love*	 Gold
1983	Motown	Lionel Richie	CAN'T SLOW DOWN	Plat.	*All Night Long* *Running With The Night* *Hello* *Stuck On You*	Gold Gold

* *Endless Love*—number one on the pop charts for 9 weeks. Also included on *DIANA ROSS GREATEST HITS* Lp (Motown Records) 1980.

** *Lady*—written by Lionel Richie, recorded by Kenny Rogers for *KENNY ROGERS GREATEST HITS* Lp (Liberty Records) 1980. Sold over 15 million copies worldwide.

** *The Good Life, So In Love With You, Goin' Back To Albama, Without You In My Life*—written by Lionel Richie, recorded by Kenny Rogers for *SHARE YOUR LOVE* Lp (Liberty Records) 1981.

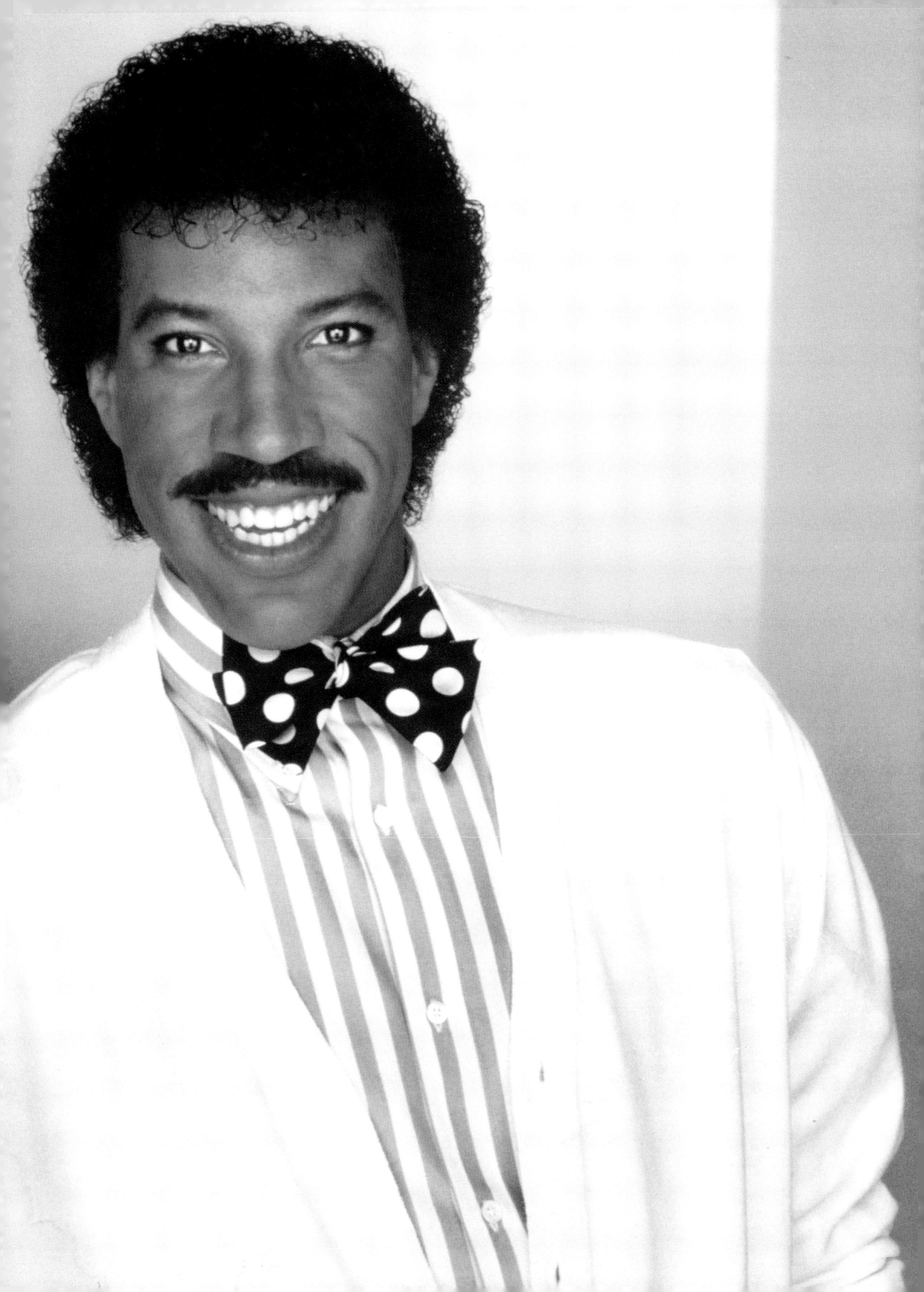

THIS IS YOUR LIFE
(August 18, 1975)*

Words and Music by
Lionel Richie

*Date of single release

C/D Dm7 Gm7 Am7 C/D Gm7
Db/Eb Ebm7 Abm7 Bbm7 Db/Eb Abm7
be strong and tell the world you're free.
Am7 C/D Dm7
Bbm7 Db/Eb Ebm7
I see the chil - dren of the world
Gm7 Am7 C/D Gm7
Abm7 Bbm7 Db/Eb Abm7
search - ing to find them - selves and who they are.
Am7 C/D Dm7
Bbm7 Db/Eb Ebm7
So man - y roads for them to choose, yeah,

Gm7
Am7
Gm7
Am7
Abm7
Bbm7
Abm7
Bbm7
so man - y ways for them to win or lose.
Oh,
Fmaj7
Em7
C
G/B
Gbmaj7
Fm7
Db
Ab/C
this is your life, oh
Bb
F
C
G/B
Bb
F
Cb
Gb
Db
Ab/C
Cb
Gb
yeah, yeah this is your life, yeah, yeah.
D
A/C#
C
G
Eb
Bb/D
Db
Ab
I feel that now in your wisdom

D A/C♯ C G
E♭ B♭/D D♭ A♭
Where do you go? Tell me, where do you go?
D A/C♯ C G
E♭ B♭/D D♭ A♭
Just see the light shine through your window.
D A/C♯ C G
E♭ B♭/D D♭ A♭
Why can't you see? Tell me now why can't you see?
D A/C♯ C G
E♭ B♭/D D♭ A♭

D A/C♯ C G
E♭ B♭/D D♭ A♭
I'm longin' to see if your search will find
peace of mind, peace of mind.
D A C G
E♭ B♭ D♭ A♭
Repeat and fade
This is your life, yeah, yeah.

SWEET LOVE
(November 25, 1975)

Moderately slow (♩ = 104)

Words and Music by
Lionel Richie

Fmaj7 Cmaj7
Gbmaj7 Dbmaj7
and all the things you wish come true, yeah;
Fmaj7 Cmaj7
Gbmaj7 Dbmaj7
I'd wish the world had all hap - py peo - ple, then
Fmaj7 Em7 Dm7 Dm7/G
Gbmaj7 Fm7 Ebm7 Ebm7/Ab
there'd be no more wish - ing to do, Oh,
C G/B F
Db Ab/C Gb
Oh, sweet love, Oh,

C
G/B
F
D♭
A♭/C
G♭
oh,
sweet love,
Oh
C
G/B
B♭
F
D♭
A♭/C
C♭
G♭
oh
ooh
3
3
Cmaj7
Fmaj7
Cmaj7
D♭maj7
G♭maj7
D♭maj7

Fmaj7
Gbmaj7
Cmaj7
Dbmaj7
Sweet love that comes through the a - ges
Fmaj7
Gbmaj7
Cmaj7
Dbmaj7
reach out and touch my soul,
Fmaj7
Gbmaj7
Cmaj7
Dbmaj7
Give my life so much mean - ing and
Fmaj7
Gbmaj7
Em7
Fm7
Dm7
Ebm7
Dm7/G
Ebm7/Ab
C
Db
G/B
Ab/C
ev - 'ry - one a heart of gold, Oh, oh

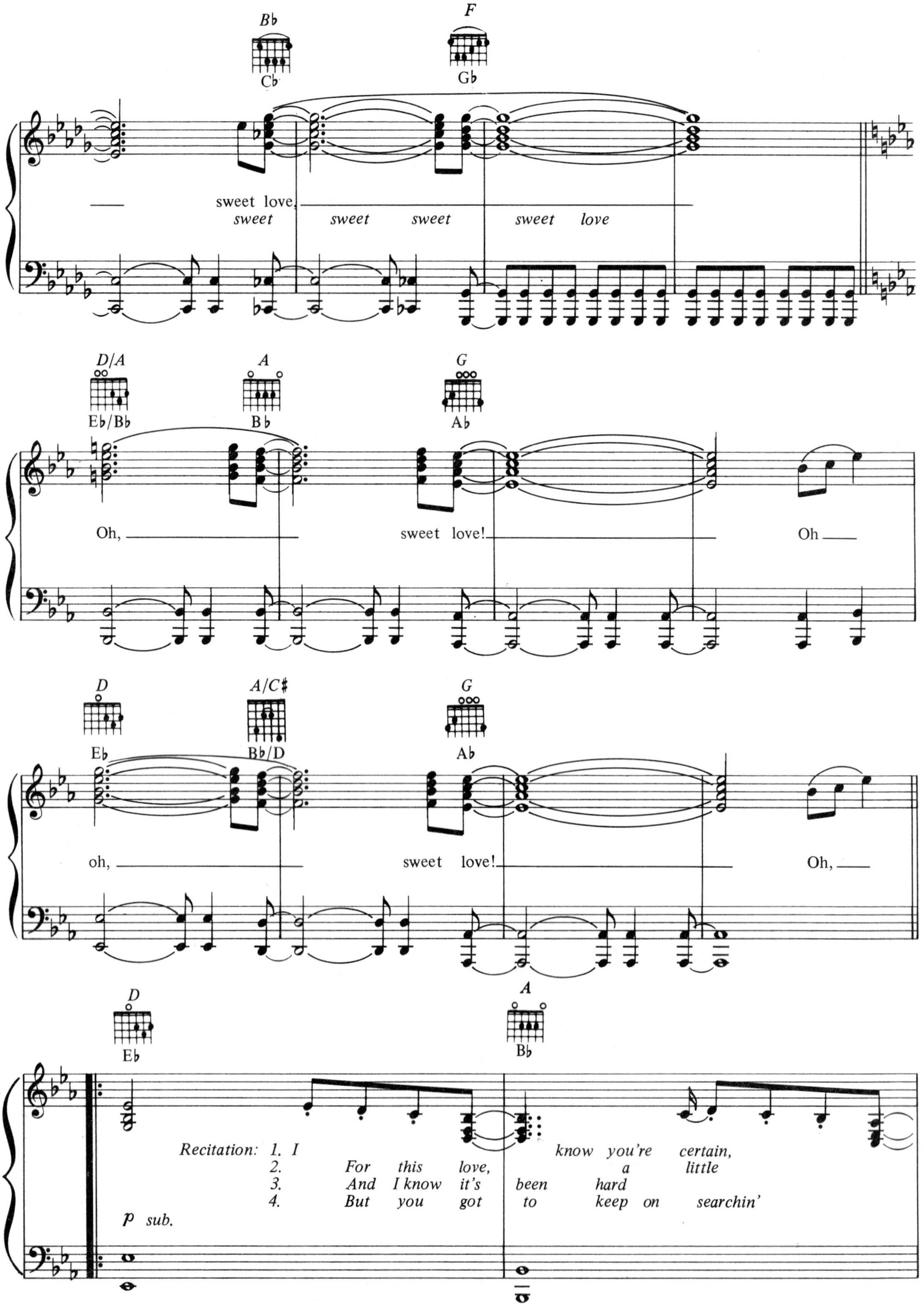
B♭
F
C♭
G♭
sweet love,
sweet sweet sweet sweet love
D/A
A
G
E♭/B♭
B♭
A♭
Oh,
sweet love!
Oh
D
A/C♯
G
E♭
B♭/D
A♭
oh,
sweet love!
Oh,
D
A
E♭
B♭
Recitation: 1. I
know you're certain,
2. For this love, a little
3. And I know it's been hard
4. But you got to keep on searchin'
p sub.

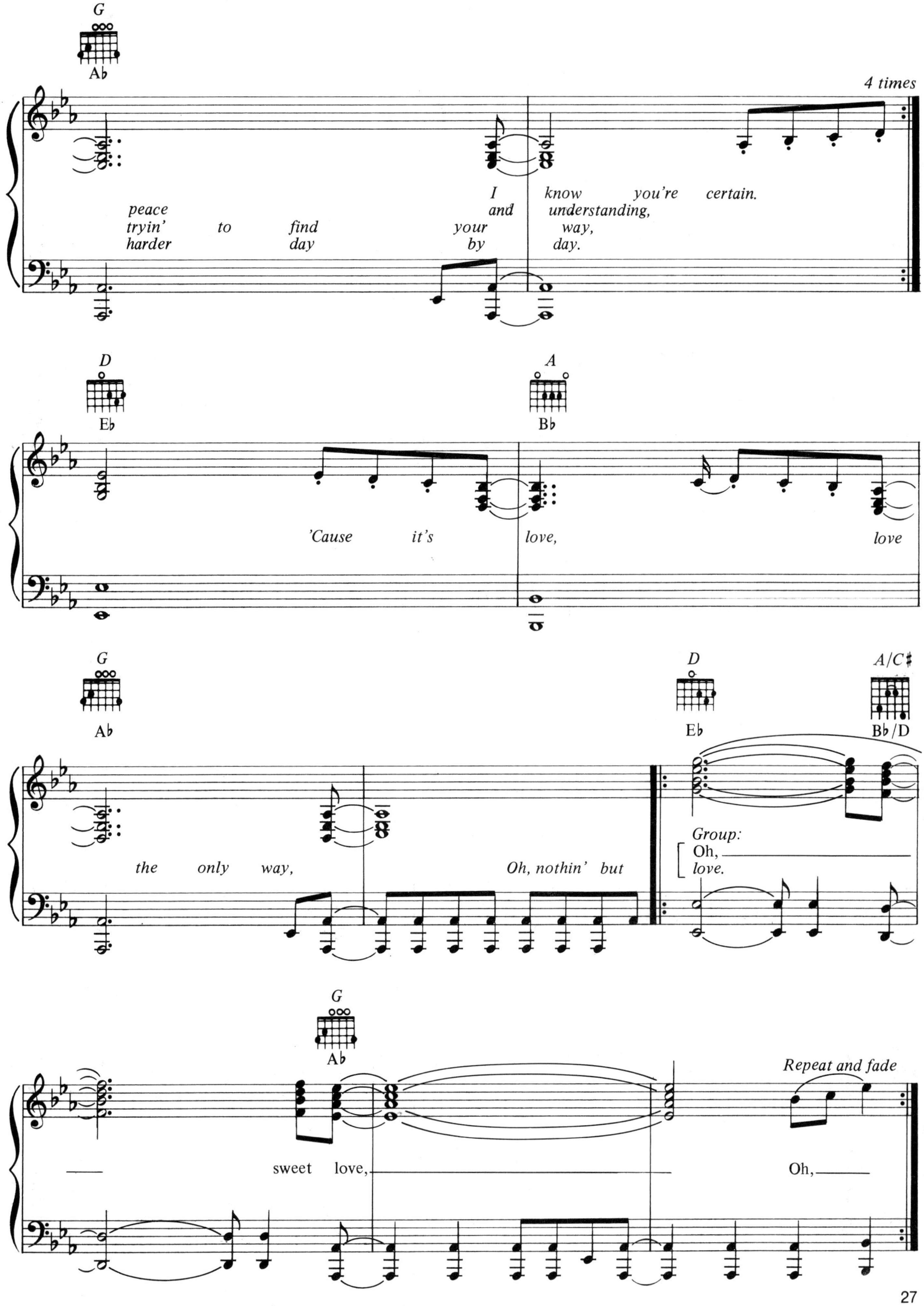
G
Ab
4 times
I know you're certain.
peace and understanding,
tryin' to find your way,
harder day by day.
D
Eb
A
Bb
'Cause it's love, love
G
Ab
D
Eb
A/C#
Bb/D
the only way, Oh, nothin' but
Group:
Oh,
love.
G
Ab
Repeat and fade
sweet love,
Oh,

JUST TO BE CLOSE TO YOU

(August 12, 1976)

Words and Music by
Lionel Richie

Slowly (♩. = 66)

C Em/G Fmaj7 Em7 Dm7/G
Ooh, we'll be alone you and me,
C Em/G Fmaj7 Em7 Dm7
Girl, we'll live our lives together, yeah, to-
Dm7/G
To Coda
gether, Oh, together! Just to be
C G/B Am Am/G
close to you, girl, just for a

Fmaj7 C/E Dm7 Dm7/G G7
mo - ment, well, just for an hour. Just to be
C G/B Am Am/G
close to you, girl.
Fmaj7 C/E Dm7 Dm7/G
C G/B Am G F G7
I been out there searchin' so very long, baby,

C G/B Am G F G7 C G/B Am
searchin' to find somebody just like you. And for some folks
G F G7 C G/B Am G F Dm7/G
D.S. al Coda
it takes a lifetime, sugar, to find in this world a dream come true. Why don't ya
Coda
C G/B Am Am/G
close__ to__ you, girl,__ for the
F C/E Dm7 Dm7/G
mo - ment, ba - by, for the mo - ment, ba - by, for the mo - ment, ba - by, for the, su - gar, su - gar, yeah, yeah,

C
G/B
Am
Am/G
yeah, yeah, yeah, yeah, yeah! Ooo
Yeah, yeah, yeah,
F
C/E
Dm7
Dm7/G
G7
yeah, yeah, yeah, etc.
Just to be
C
G/B
Am
Am/G
close to you, girl,
just for a
Repeat and fade
Fmaj7
C/E
Dm7
Dm7/G
G7
mo - ment, well, just for an
hour...
Just to be

HIGH ON SUNSHINE
(Album date: June 15, 1976)

Words and Music by
Thomas McClary and Lionel Richie

Moderately slow (♩= 96)

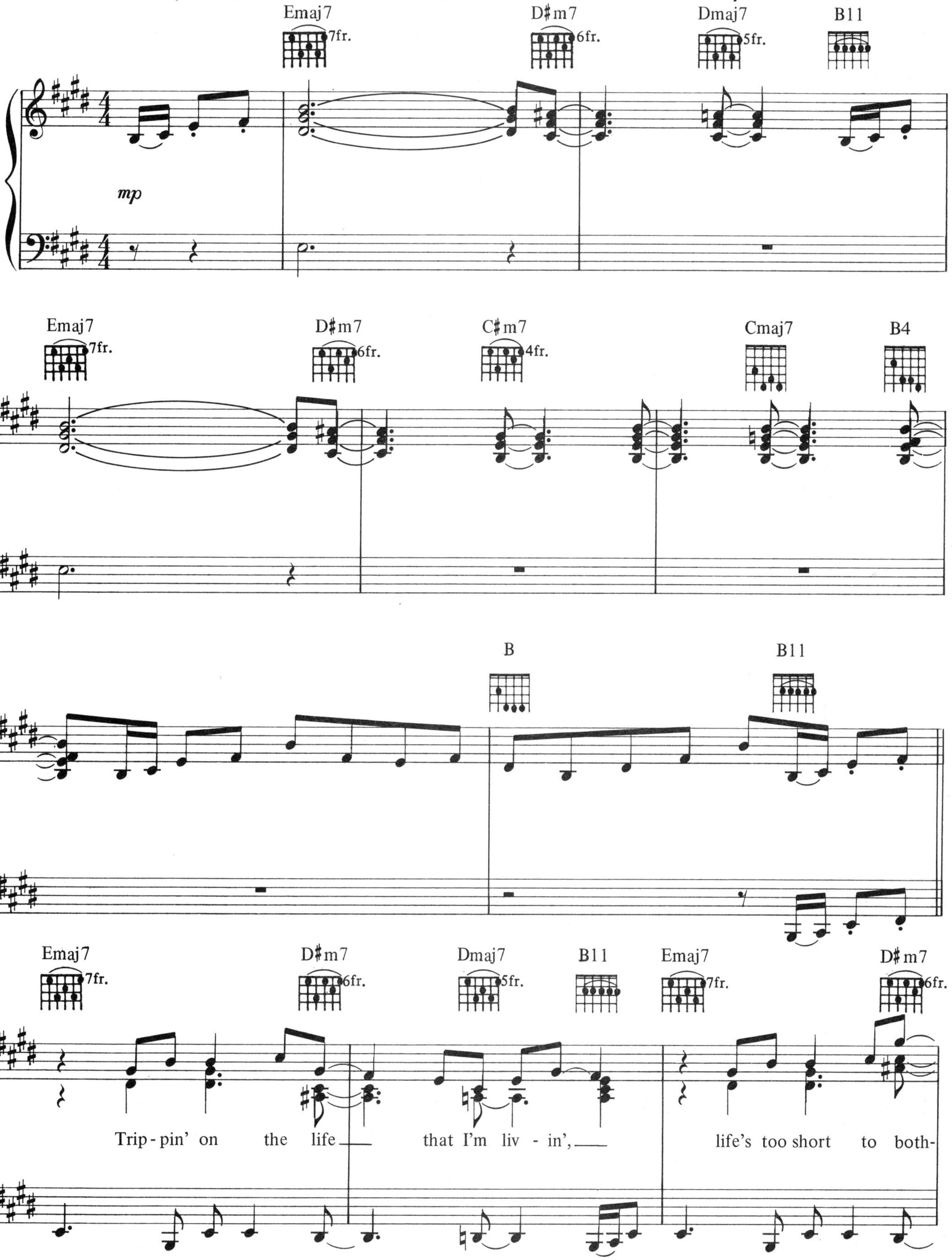

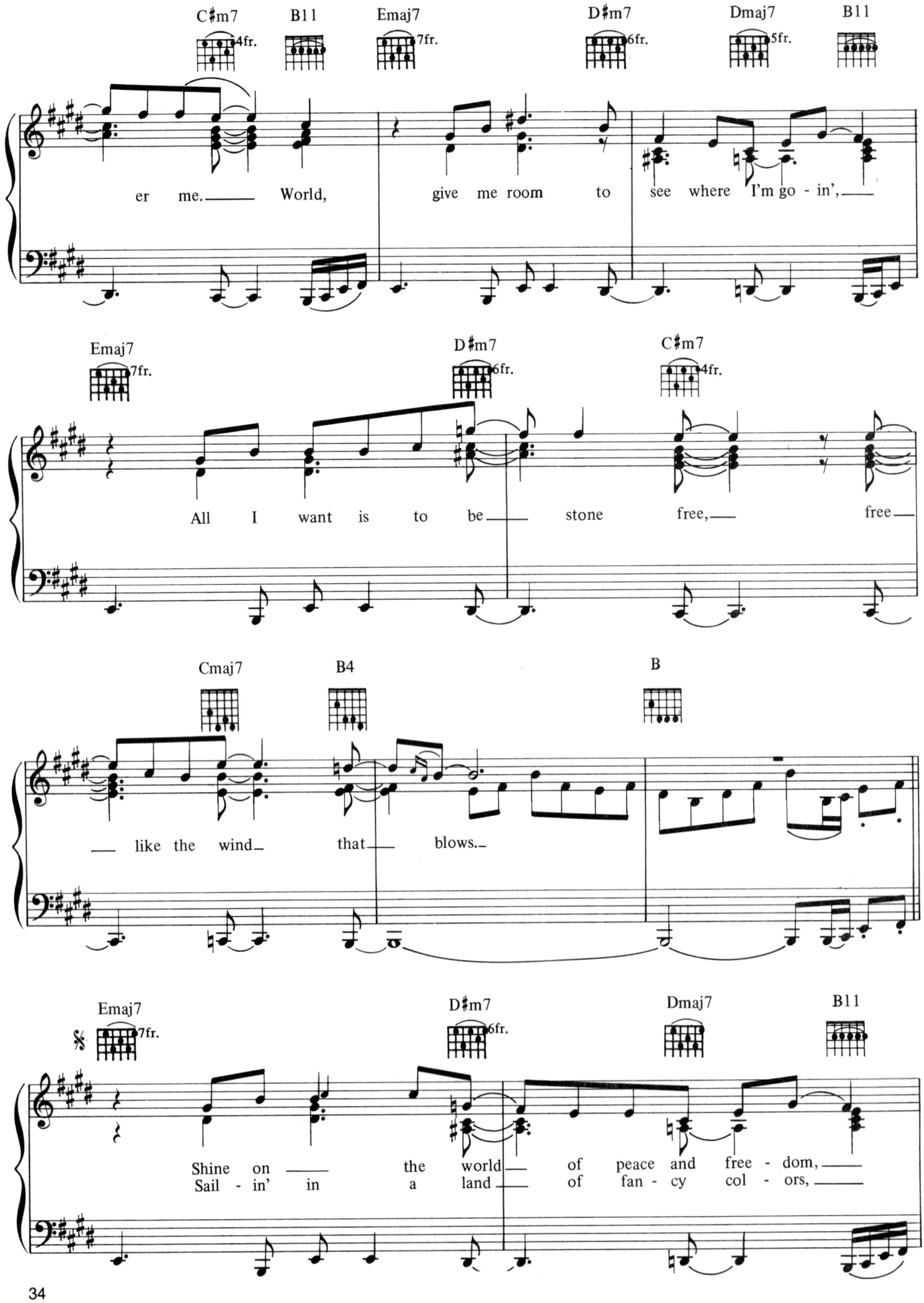
C♯m7 B11 Emaj7 D♯m7 Dmaj7 B11
4fr. 7fr. 6fr. 5fr.
er me. World, give me room to see where I'm go - in',
Emaj7 D♯m7 C♯m7
7fr. 6fr. 4fr.
All I want is to be stone free, free
Cmaj7 B4 B
like the wind that blows.
Emaj7 D♯m7 Dmaj7 B11
7fr. 6fr.
Shine on the world of peace and free - dom,
Sail - in' in a land of fan - cy col - ors,

Emaj7
7fr.
D♯m7
6fr.
C♯m7
4fr.
B11
shine on you peo - ple hard as stone, yeah.
I see the world thru rain - bow shades, yeah.
Emaj7
7fr.
D♯m7
6fr.
Dmaj7
5fr.
B11
I hope you see the storm that's in the val - ley,
But peo - ple make my col - ors such a has - sle,
Emaj7
7fr.
D♯m7
6fr.
C♯m7
4fr.
I hope you see your right from wrong; O -
some - times I wish they'd all fade a - way; Chang-
Cmaj7
B4
B
G♯7/B♯
pen your minds and see, wo - oh!
es we all go through. Wo well.

C♯m
4fr.
F♯m
Work so hard for mon - ey, (for the mon - ey) but
I don't need no doc - tor (no doc - tor) to
C♯m
4fr.
F♯m
mon - ey on - ly buys me pain. (so much pain) Now - a
give me my peace of mind. (peace of mind)
C♯m
4fr.
F♯m
Amaj7
5fr.
D♯7
4fr.
I'm free and eas - y
I'm free for - ev - er
'cause I'm - a high on
G♯m7
4fr.
C♯7
Amaj7
5fr.
D♯7
4fr.
G♯m7
4fr.
sun - shine,
light my way,

Amaj7
5fr.
D♯7
4fr.
G♯m7
4fr.
C♯7
F♯m7
High on sun - shine; take
B4
Cmaj7
B11
all my dreams a - way.
ooh
*
Emaj7
7fr.
D♯m7
6fr.
C♯m7
4fr.
ooo
Emaj7
7fr.
D♯m7
6fr.
Dmaj7
5fr.
D.S. and fade at *
N.C.

FANCY DANCER
(November 24, 1976)

Words and Music by
Ronald LaPread and Lionel Richie

Moderate Funk (♩ = 102)

such a real good feelin' to have, the
I love the way you twist and turn your body; doll,
kind of feelin' good lovin' brings. Yeah!
you're like a puppet on a string. Yeah!
Put your head on my shoulder,
Sugar baby, sugar baby,
my head's a-spinning around and around,
Just like a fox walkin' down the block,

I hear the sound of sweet funky music
drive me crazy . . . sexy lady.
even when there ain't no sound, yeah!
You're so bad there's only one thing I can say: that you're my
These bars first time only
Vi - sions of you, my love, dancin' in my head. The
stars in my life, girl, on-ly one thing can be said: That you're my

fan - cy danc - er,
fan - cy danc - er. You're my
fan - cy danc - er,
fan - cy danc - er. You're my
fan - cy danc - er,
fan - cy danc - er. You're my
fan - cy danc - er, Yeah!
Ooh
8va

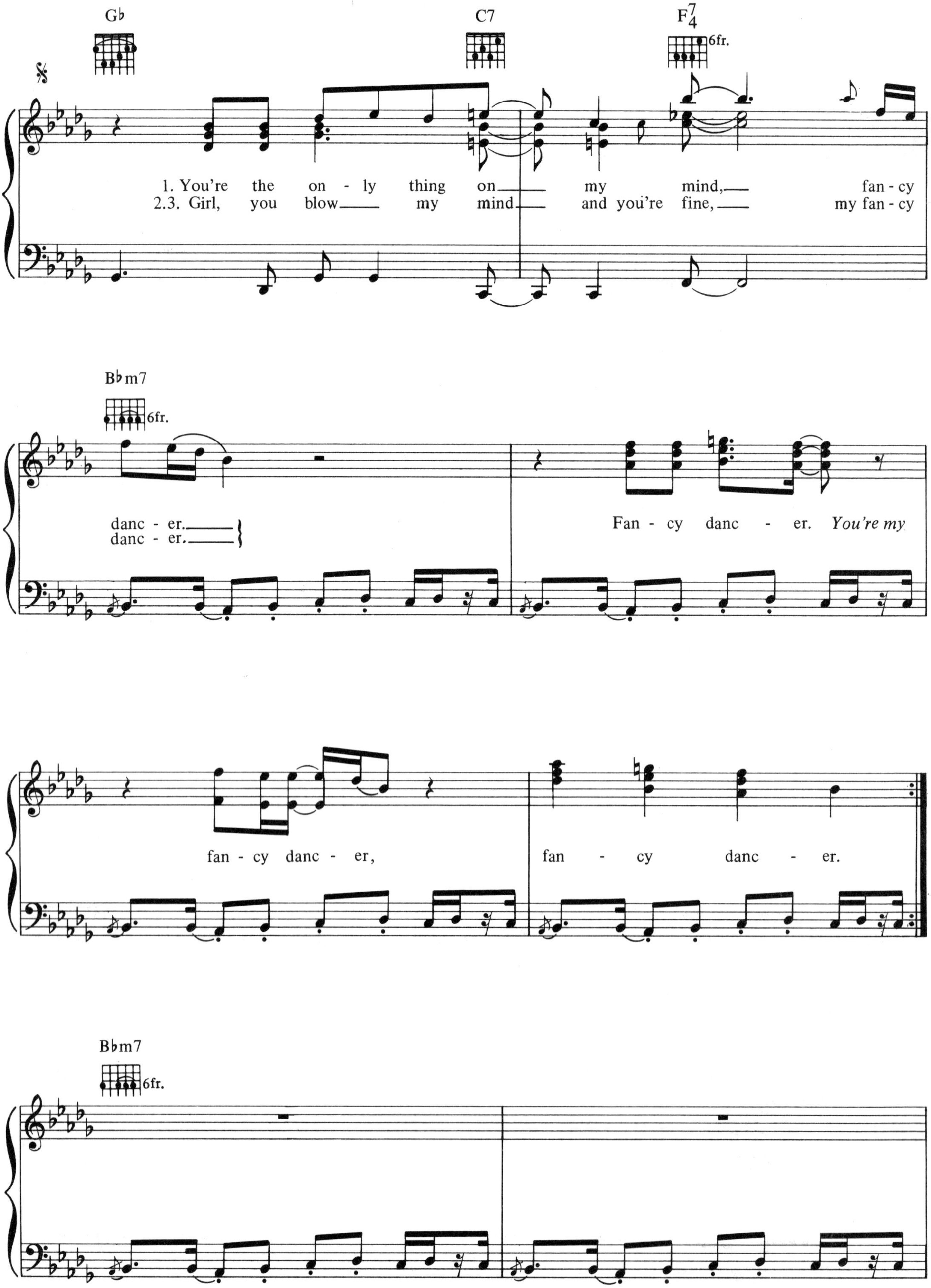
G♭
C7
F7 4
6fr.
1. You're the on - ly thing on my mind, fan - cy
2.3. Girl, you blow my mind and you're fine, my fan - cy
B♭m7
6fr.
danc - er.
danc - er.
Fan - cy danc - er. You're my
fan - cy danc - er,
fan - cy danc - er.
B♭m7
6fr.

Love me! Ooo
Thrill me! Ooo
oh you're my
Fan - cy . . .
D.S. and fade
Fan - cy . . .
Aw, girl, come on and do it to me. Yeah!

EASY
(May 5, 1977)

Words and Music by
Lionel Richie

G Bm Am7 Am7/D
Ab Cm Bbm7 Bbm7/Eb
You see, I begged, stole_and I bor - rowed._ Yeah,_ ooh. That's why I'm eas-
G Bm7 Am7 Am7/D G Bm7
Ab Cm7 Bbm7 Bbm7/Eb Ab Cm7
- y, (Ah) I'm eas - y like Sun-day morn - ing. (Ah
Am7 Am7/D G Bm7
Bbm7 Bbm7/Eb Ab Cm7
) That's why I'm eas - y,
Am7 Am7/D F C/E C/D G
Bbm7 Bbm7/Eb Gb Db/F Db/Eb Ab
I'm eas - y like Sun - day morn - ing.

G Bm Am7 Am7/D
A♭ Cm B♭m7 B♭m7/E♭
Why in the world_would an - y - bod - y put chains___ on me?_
G Bm Am7 Am7/D
A♭ Cm B♭m7 B♭m7/E♭
3
I've paid_ my dues_ to make it.___
G Bm Am7 Am7/D
A♭ Cm B♭m7 B♭m7/E♭
Ev - 'ry - bod - y wants_me to be__ what they want__ me to be;_
G Bm Am7 Am7/D
A♭ Cm B♭m7 B♭m7/E♭
I'm not hap - py when I try to fake__ it,__ no_ Ooh,_ that's why I'm eas-

G Bm7 Am7 Am7/D
Ab Cm7 Bbm7 Bbm7/Eb
- y, (Ah) I'm eas - y like Sun - day morn -
G Bm7 Am7 Am7/D
Ab Cm7 Bbm7 Bbm7/Eb
- ing. (Ah) That's why I'm eas -
G Bm7 Am7 Am7/D
Ab Cm7 Bbm7 Bbm7/Eb
- y, I'm eas - y like Sun - day morn
F C/E C/D G
Gb Db/F Db/Eb Ab
- - ing. I wan - na be

* Instrumental solo omitted

BRICK HOUSE
(August 11, 1976)

Words and Music by
Lionel Richie, Ronald LaPread,
Walter Orange, Milan Williams,
Thomas McClary & William King

Moderately and Funky (♩ = 108)

brick house,
Ah, that
la - dy's stacked, and that's a fact,
ain't hold - in' noth - in' back. Oh, she's a
brick house.
Well,
we're to - geth - er ev - 'ry - bod - y knows.
This is how the sto - ry goes:

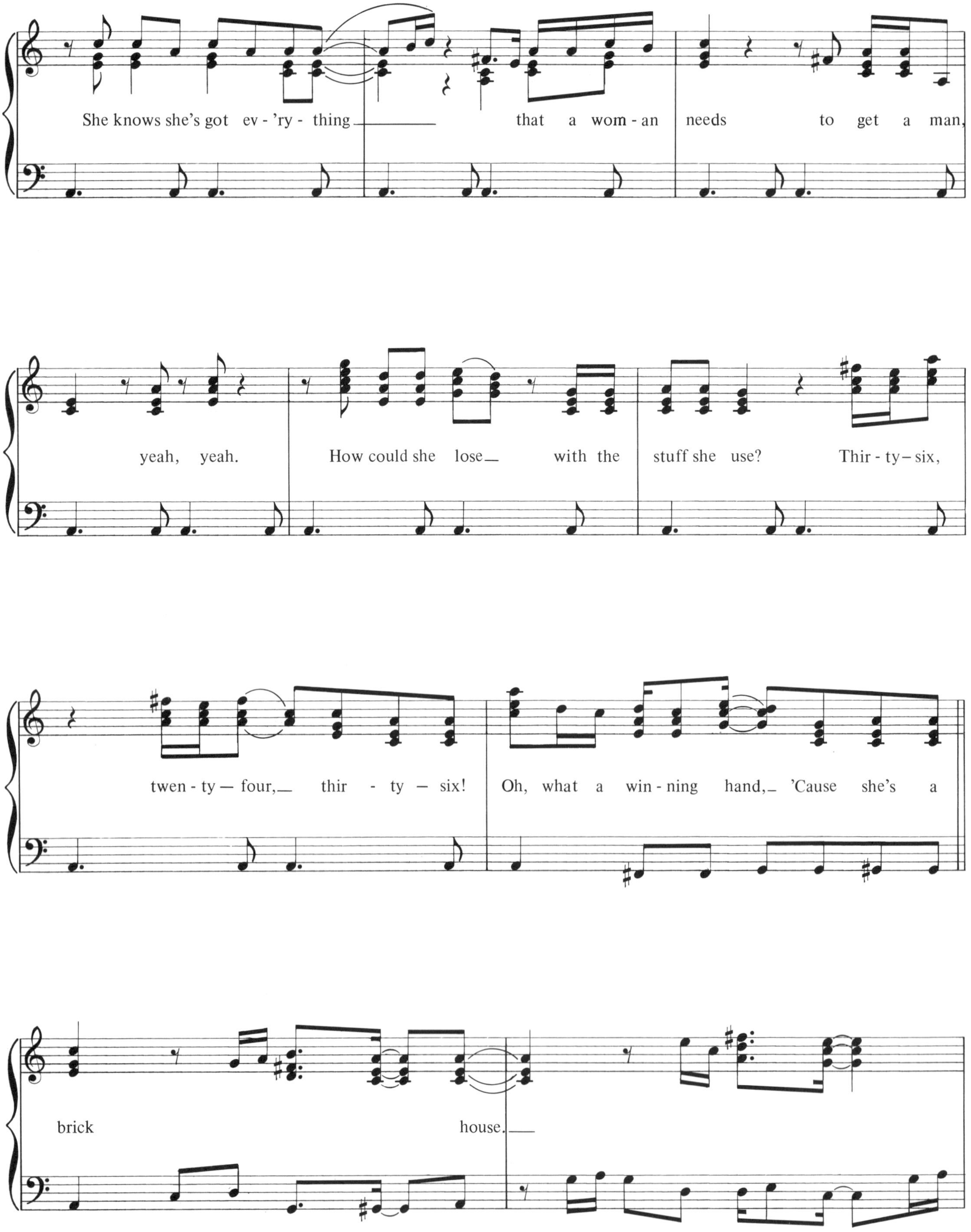
She knows she's got ev - 'ry - thing that a wom - an needs to get a man,
yeah, yeah. How could she lose with the stuff she use? Thir - ty - six,
twen - ty — four, thir - ty — six! Oh, what a win - ning hand, 'Cause she's a
brick house.

She's might - y, might - y just
let - tin' it all hang out. Ah, she's a
brick house.
Ow, that
la - dy's stacked and that's a fact,
ain't hold - in' noth - in' back. Oh, she's a
brick
house.
Yeah.

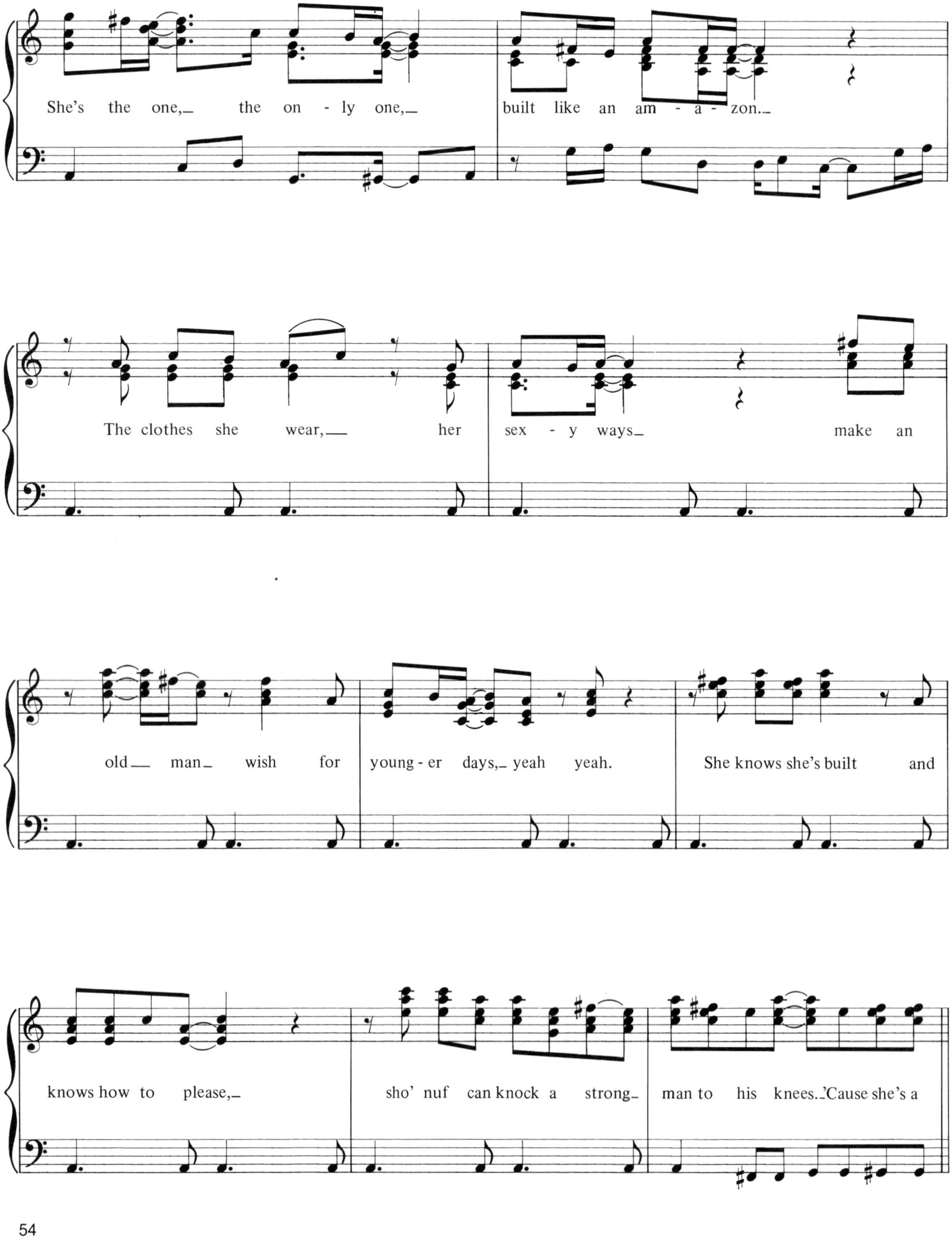
She's the one, the on - ly one,
built like an am - a - zon.
The clothes she wear, her
sex - y ways make an
old man wish for
young - er days, yeah yeah.
She knows she's built and
knows how to please,
sho' nuf can knock a strong
man to his knees. 'Cause she's a

Am7
brick house. Yeah, she's might - y, might - y just
let - tin' it all hang out. Ah, she's a brick house. That
la - dy's stacked and that's a fact ain't hold - in' noth - in back. Ow!
1.2.3.
4.
D.S. and fade
Shook-a dow shook-a dow dow shook-a dow shook - a dow dow shook - a dow shook-a dow
mf

THREE TIMES A LADY
(June 8, 1978)

Words and Music by
Lionel Richie

Em
B7+/D♯
G
Fm
C7+/E
A♭
loud:
You're
once,
D/F♯
F
C/E
Am7
E♭/G
G♭
D♭/F
B♭m7
twice,
three times a la - dy
and I love
G
D
D/C
G
A♭
E♭
E♭/D♭
A♭
you.
Yes you're once,
twice,
D/F♯
F
C/E
Am7
E♭/G
G♭
D♭/F
B♭m7
three times a la - dy
and I love

G
D
D/C
D/B
Ab
Eb
Eb/Db
Eb/C
you,
I love
D/A
G
D/G
G
C/D
Eb/Bb
Ab
Eb/Ab
Ab
Db/Eb
you.
When
G
D/G
C6/G
C/D
Ab
Eb/Ab
Db6/Ab
Db/Eb
we are to - geth - er the mo - ments I cher - ish with
G
D/G
C6/G
C/D
Ab
Eb/Ab
Db6/Ab
Db/Eb
ev - 'ry beat of my heart, To

G D/G C6/G C/D G
Ab Eb/Ab Db6/Ab Db/Eb Ab
touch you, to hold you, to feel you, to need you, there's noth - ing to
D/G C6/G C/D G D/G
Eb/Ab Db6/Ab Db/Eb Ab Eb/Ab
keep us a - part.
C6/G D/G C/G
Db6/Ab Eb/Ab Db/Ab
G D/G C/G
Ab Eb/Ab Db/Ab
Ooo ooo ooo ooo
3

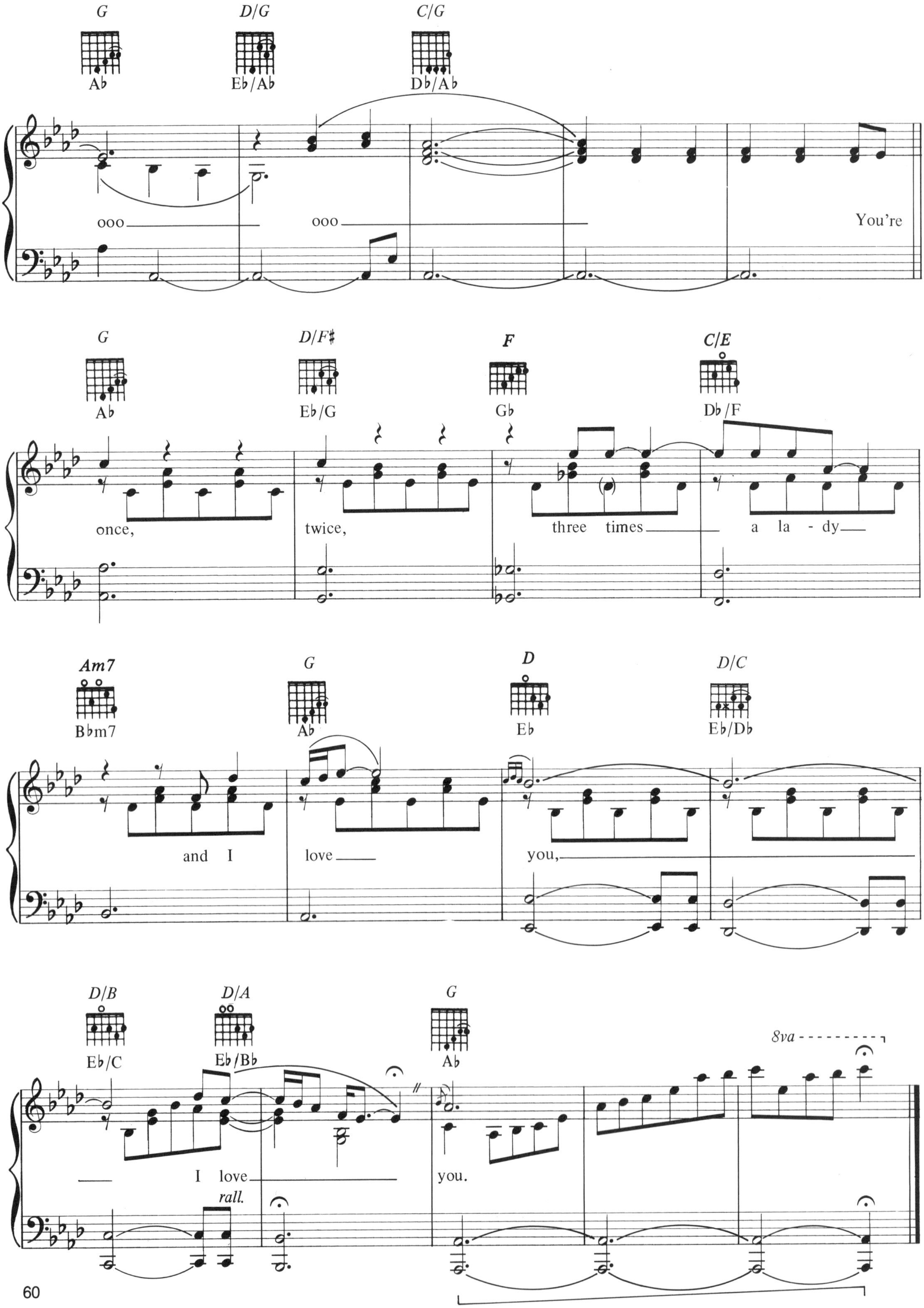
G
D/G
C/G
Ab
Eb/Ab
Db/Ab
ooo
ooo
You're
G
D/F♯
F
C/E
Ab
Eb/G
Gb
Db/F
once,
twice,
three times
a la - dy
Am7
G
D
D/C
Bbm7
Ab
Eb
Eb/Db
and I
love
you,
D/B
D/A
G
Eb/C
Eb/Bb
Ab
8va
I love
rall.
you.

SAIL ON
(July 27, 1979)

Words and Music by
Lionel Richie

Moderately (♩ = 76)
Guitar → C
(Capo up 1 fret)
Piano → D♭
Dm
E♭m
mp
C
D♭
C
D♭
Dm
E♭m
Sail on down the line 'bout a half a mile or so, and - a
Sail on down the line. Ain't it fun - ny how the time can go on - a?

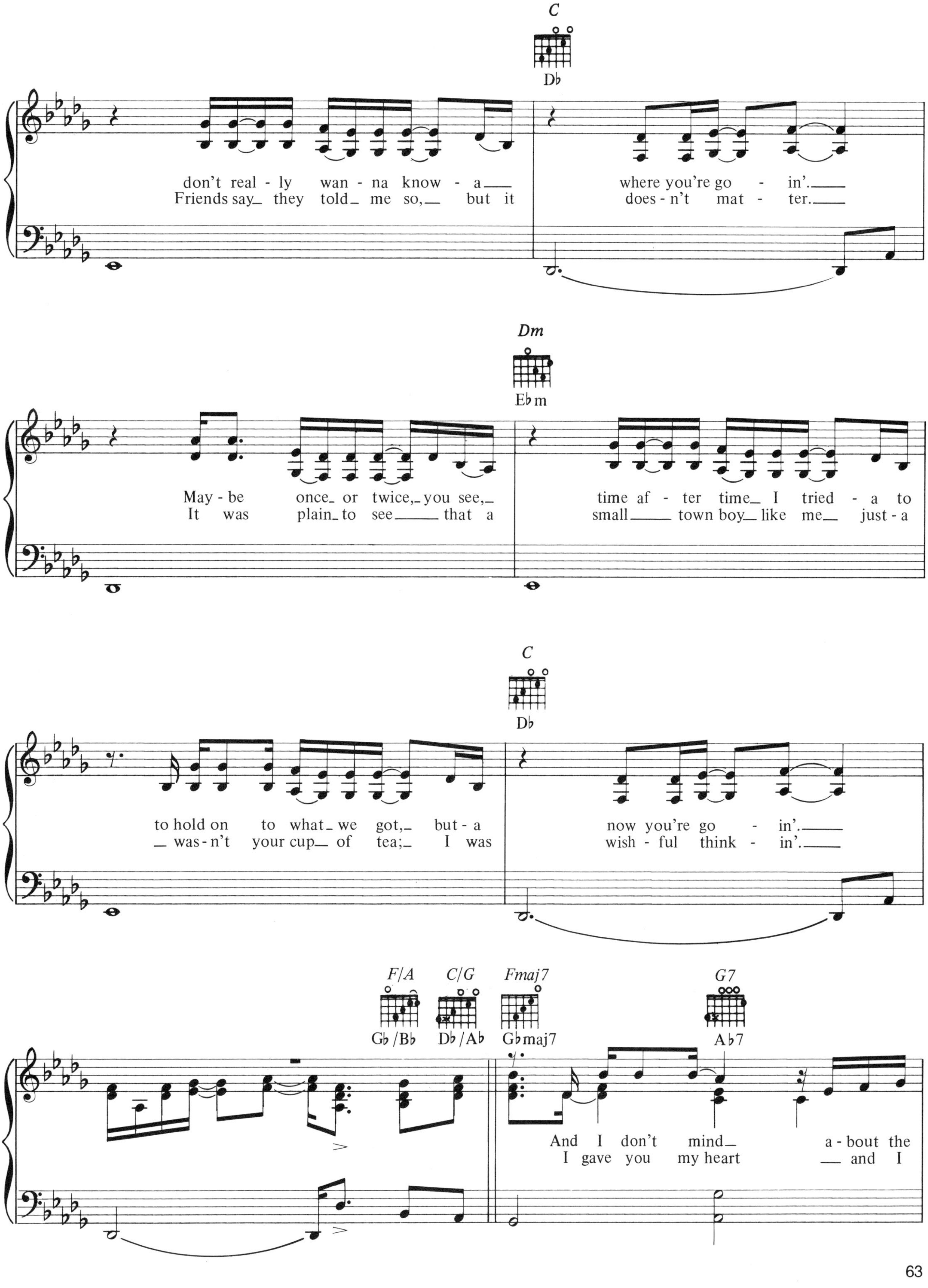
C
D♭
don't real - ly wan - na know - a where you're go - in'.
Friends say they told me so, but it does - n't mat - ter.
Dm
E♭m
May - be once or twice, you see, time af - ter time I tried - a to
It was plain to see that a small town boy like me just - a
C
D♭
to hold on to what we got, but - a now you're go - in'.
was - n't your cup of tea; I was wish - ful think - in'.
F/A
C/G
Fmaj7
G7
G♭/B♭
D♭/A♭
G♭maj7
A♭7
And I don't mind a - bout the
I gave you my heart and I

C G/B Am7 Fmaj7 G7
Db Ab/C Bbm7 Gbmaj7 Ab7
things you're gon - na say, Lord; I gave all my mon - ey and my
tried to make you hap - py, And you gave me noth - in' in re -
C G/B Am7 Fmaj7 G7
Db Ab/C Bbm7 Gbmaj7 Ab7
time. I know it's a shame but I'm
turn. You know, it ain't so hard to say, "Would you
C G/B Am7 Cmaj7/G Fmaj7
Db Ab/C Bbm7 Dbmaj7/Ab Gbmaj7
giv - in' you back your name! Yeah, yeah,
please just go a - way!" Yeah, yeah,
Em F C/E Dm F C/E Dm
Fm Gb Db/F Ebm Gb Db/F Ebm
yes, I'll be on my way; I won't be back to stay,
I've thrown a - way the blues, I'm tired of be - in' used,

F Em Dm7 Dm7/G C G
Gb Fm Ebm7 Ebm7/Ab Db Ab
1.
(D.C.)
I guess I'll move_ a-long;_ I'm look-in' for a good_ time_
I want ev-'ry-one_ to know_ I'm look-in' for a good_ time,
2.
Bb F G
Cb Gb Ab
_ good time_
Wo-oh,
Fmaj7 Em7
Gbmaj7 Fm7
sail on, hon-ey,
Sail on, su-gar,
Repeat and fade
Fmaj7 Em7 Dm7 Dm7/G
Gbmaj7 Fm7 Ebm7 Ebm7/Ab
good times_ nev-er felt so_ good._

STILL
(September 14, 1979)

Words and Music by
Lionel Richie

A4 A Dmaj7
Db4 Db Gbmaj7
you said you've nev - er need - ed me; I
E7/4 E7 E7/4 E7 A4/2 A G/F# A7/E
Ab7/4 Ab7 Ab7/4 Ab7 Db4/2 Db Cb/Bb Db7/Ab
won - der if you need me now. So man - y
Dmaj7 Bm7 E7 Amaj7
Gbmaj7 Ebm7 Ab7 Dbmaj7
dreams that flew a - way, so man - y words we did - n't say.
A9 G/F# A7/E Dmaj7 Bm7 E7
Db9 Cb/Bb Db7/Ab Gbmaj7 Ebm7 Ab7
Two peo - ple lost in a storm, where did we

Amaj7 A9 G/F♯ A7/E Dmaj7
D♭maj7 D♭9 C♭/B♭ D♭7/A♭ G♭maj7
3
go, where'd we go? Lost what we both had found,
Bm7 E7 Amaj7
E♭m7 A♭7 D♭maj7
you know we let each oth - er down.
3
A9 G/F♯ A7/E Dmaj7 D Bm7
D♭9 C♭/B♭ D♭7/A♭ G♭maj7 G♭ E♭m7
But then most of all I do love you
E A4/2 A
A♭ D♭4/2 D♭
Black key gliss
gliss.
(whisper) still.
f

Dmaj7
Gbmaj7
E7/4 E7 E7/4 E7 A4/2 A
Ab7/4 Ab7 Ab7/4 Ab7 Db4/2 Db
A7 G/F# A7/E
Db7 Cb/Bb Db7/Ab
We played the
Dmaj7 Bm7 E7 Amaj7
Gbmaj7 Ebm7 Ab7 Dbmaj7
games — that peo - ple play, we made — our mis - takes — a - long the way.
A7 G/F# A7/E Dmaj7 Bm7 E7
Db7 Cb/Bb Db7/Ab Gbmaj7 Ebm7 Ab7
Some - how I know deep in my heart you need - ed

Amaj7 A9 G/F♯ A7/E Dmaj7
D♭maj7 D♭9 C♭/B♭ D♭7/A♭ G♭maj7
me, 'cause I need - ed you so des - p'rate - ly,
Bm7 E7 Amaj7
E♭m7 A♭7 D♭maj7
We were too blind to see.
A9 G/F♯ A7/E Dmaj7 D Bm7
D♭9 C♭/B♭ D♭7/A♭ G♭maj7 G♭ E♭m7
But then most of all, I do love you
E A$\frac{4}{2}$ A
A♭ D♭$\frac{4}{2}$ D♭
still.

HEROES
(August 22, 1980)

Words and Music by
Lionel Richie, and Darrell P. Jones

Em11
mp
Look - in' back through time we are in
Bm7
Am7
Am7/D
Em11
debt to the lead - ers, an - gels of mer-
Bm7
Am7
Am7/D
- cy ev - 'ry one.
Em11
Good folks who be - lieved there was no

Bm7
Am7
Am7/D
Em11
good in e - vil
fought long and hard
Bm7
Am7
Am7/D
until the battles all were won.
Cmaj7
Bm7
E7
Cmaj7
f
He - roes make the sun rise in the morn - in',
Bm7
E7
Cmaj7
Bm7
E7
he - roes make the moon

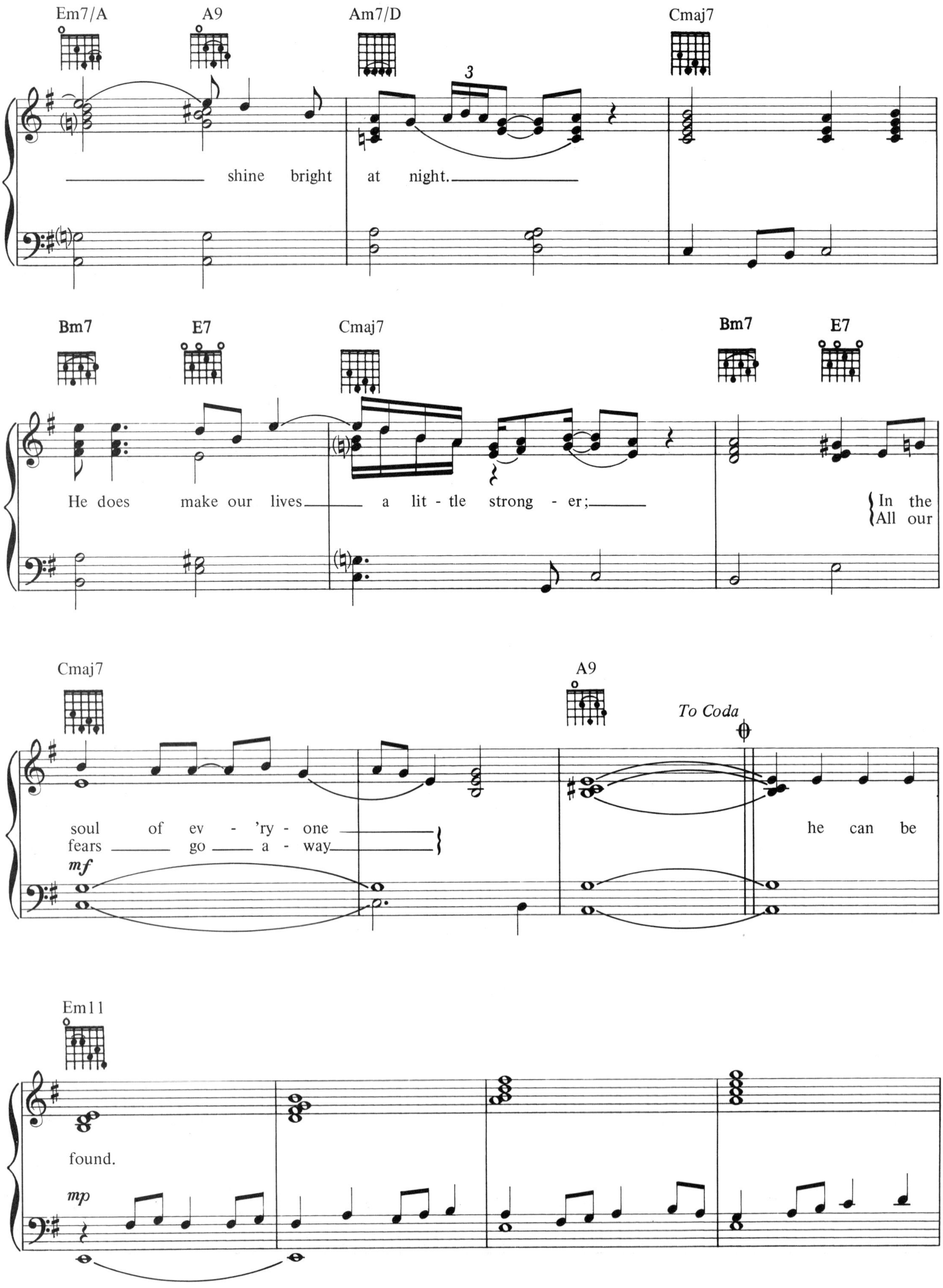
Em7/A
A9
Am7/D
Cmaj7
3
shine bright at night.
Bm7
E7
Cmaj7
Bm7
E7
He does make our lives a lit - tle strong - er;
In the
All our
Cmaj7
A9
To Coda
soul of ev - 'ry - one
fears go a - way
he can be
mf
Em11
found.
mp

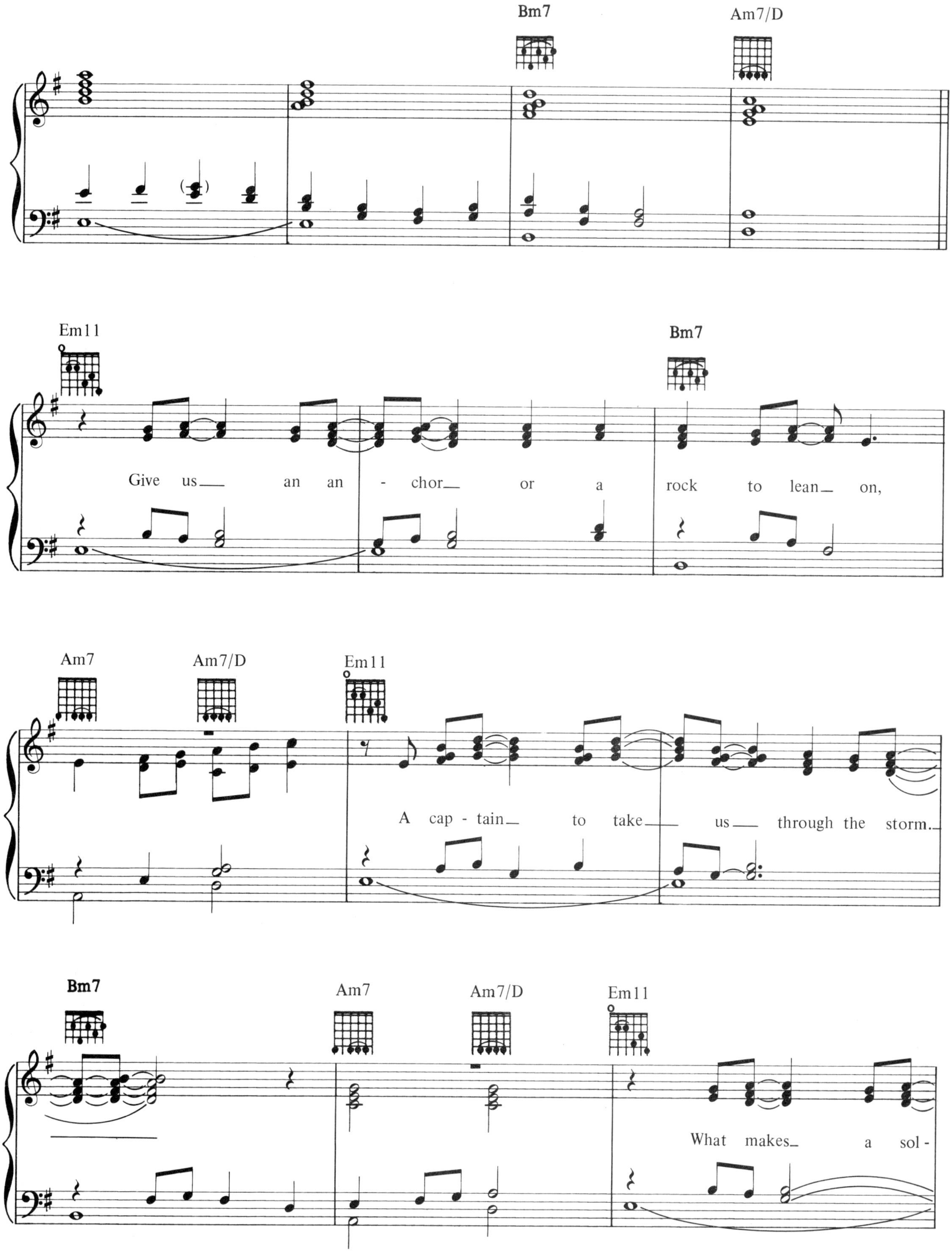
Bm7
Am7/D
Em11
Give us an an - chor or a
Bm7
rock to lean on,
Am7
Am7/D
Em11
A cap - tain to take us through the storm.
Bm7
Am7
Am7/D
Em11
What makes a sol -

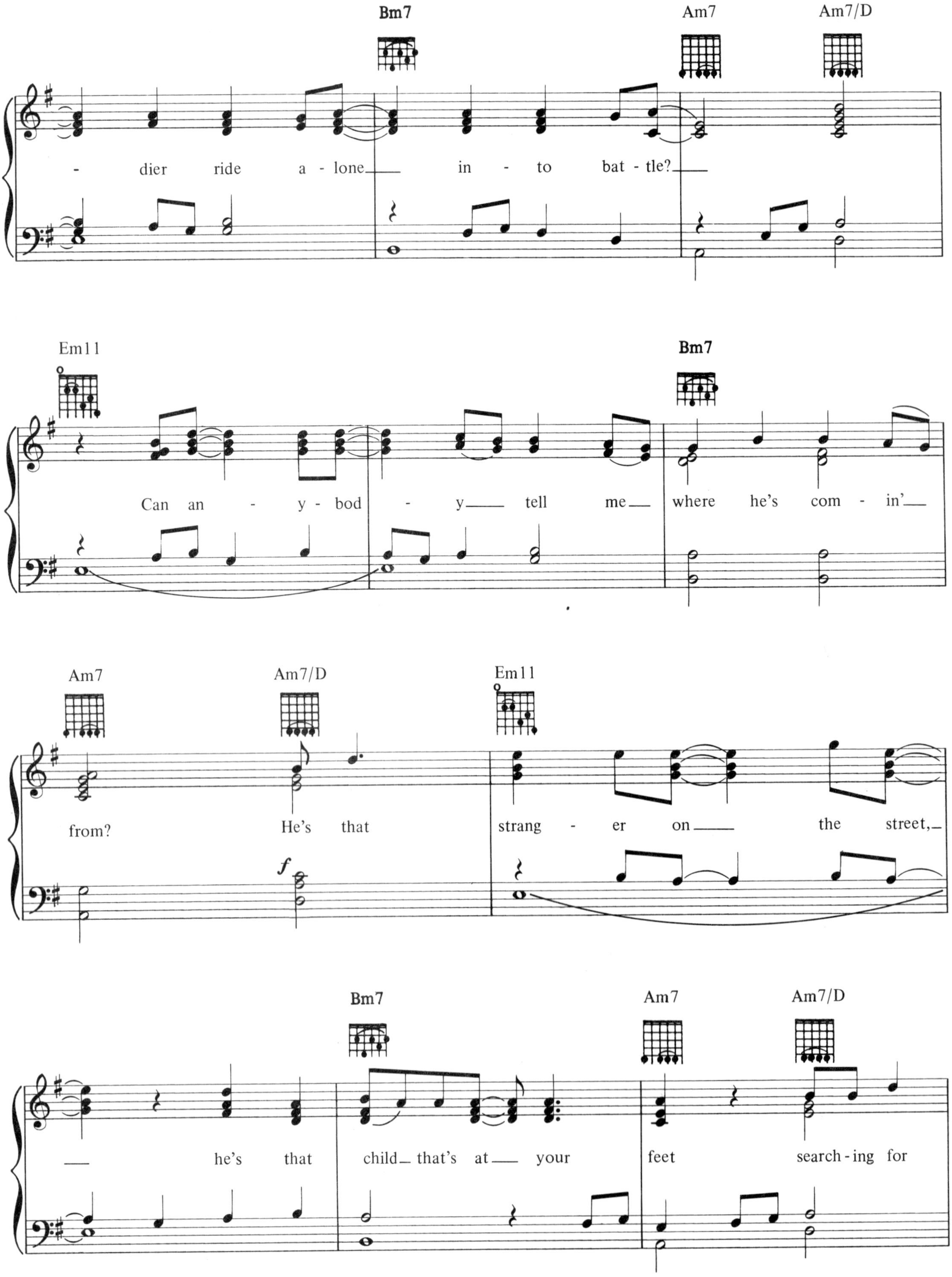
Bm7
Am7
Am7/D
- dier ride a - lone__ in - to bat - tle?__
Em11
Bm7
Can an - y - bod - y__ tell me__ where he's com - in'__
Am7
Am7/D
Em11
from? He's that strang - er on__ the street,_
f
Bm7
Am7
Am7/D
__ he's that child_ that's at__ your feet search - ing for

Em11
free - dom and jus - tice for all.
Bm7
Am7
Am7/D
Em11
We've seen them time and a - gain,
you know they
Bm7
on - ly fight to win;
Am7
Am7/D
Em11
They're the chal - leng - ers of

Bm7
Am7
Em11
D.S. al Coda
e - vil and I'm glad we know them.
Coda
Em11
when he's 'round.
Bm7
Cmaj7
Bm7
E7
Cmaj7
Bm7
E7
Cmaj7
Bm7
E7

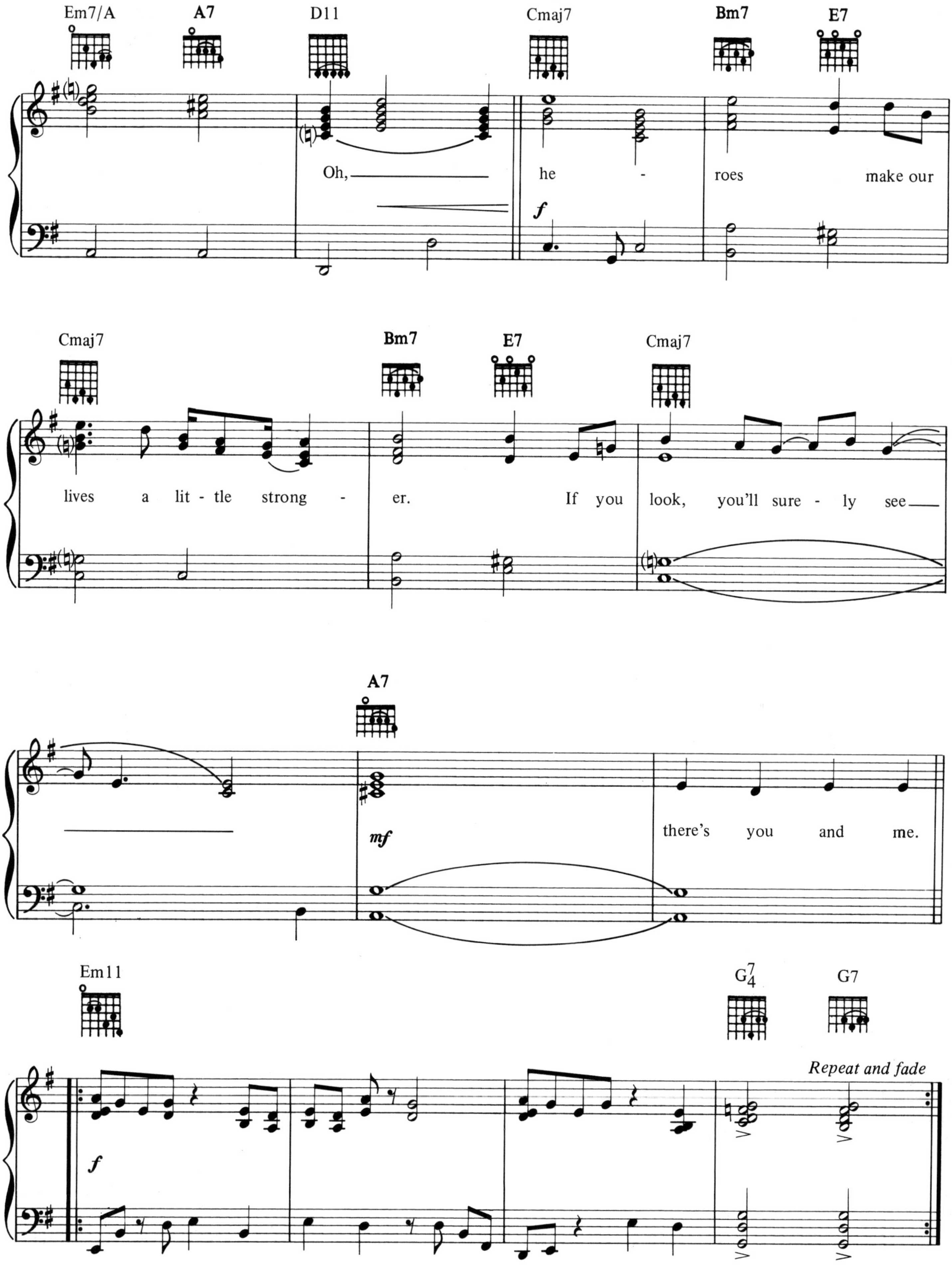
Em7/A A7 D11 Cmaj7 Bm7 E7
Oh, he - roes make our
f
Cmaj7 Bm7 E7 Cmaj7
lives a lit - tle strong - er. If you look, you'll sure - ly see
A7
mf
there's you and me.
Em11 G7/4 G7
Repeat and fade
f

JESUS IS LOVE
(November 14, 1980)

Words and Music by
Lionel Richie

G D/F♯ Em G7/D
A♭ E♭/G Fm A♭7/E♭
teach them to love one an - oth - er and heav - en might
C G/B Am7 C/D Fmaj7
D♭ A♭/C B♭m7 D♭/E♭ G♭maj7
find a place in their hearts 'cause Je -
Em7 Dm7/G C G/B Em7
Fm7 E♭m7/A♭ D♭ A♭/C Fm7
sus is love. He
Am7 C/D Fmaj7 Em7 Dm7/G
B♭m7 D♭/E♭ G♭maj7 Fm7 E♭m7/A♭
won't let you down, and I know He's

C G/B Em7 Am7 C/D
Db Ab/C Fm7 Bbm7 Db/Eb
mine forever, ah, in my
G D/F#
Ab Eb/G
heart. 2. We've got to walk on, walk on
Em7 G7/D C G/B
Fm7 Ab7/Eb Db Ab/C
through temp-ta-tion, 'cause His love and His wis-dom will
Am7 C/D G D/F#
Bbm7 Db/Eb Ab Eb/G
be our help-ing hand. And I know the truth and His word will be our

Em G7/D C G/B Am7
Fm Ab7/Eb Db Ab/C Bbm7
sal - va - tion. Lift up our hearts to be thank - ful and glad
C/D Fmaj7 Em7 Dm7/G C G/B Em7 Am7 C/D Fmaj7
Db/Eb Gbmaj7 Fm7 Ebm7/Ab Db Ab/C Fm7 Bbm7 Db/Eb Gbmaj7
that Je - sus is love. He won't let you down, and I know
Em7 Dm7/G C G/B Em7
Fm7 Ebm7/Ab Db Ab/C Fm7
He's mine for -
Am7 C/D G D/F♯
Bbm7 Db/Eb Ab Eb/G
ev - er, ah, in my heart, help me heart, heart.

Em7 G7 C G/B
Fm7 Ab7 Db Ab/C
I know, I
Am7 C/D G D/F♯ Bm7
Bbm7 Db/Eb Ab Eb/G Cm7
know, I know, I know His love's the pow - er, His love's the glo - ry for -
Em7 G7 C G/B Am7 C/D
Fm7 Ab7 Db Ab/C Bbm7 Db/Eb
ev - er.
G D/F♯ Em G7/D C G/B
Ab Eb/G Fm Ab7/Eb Db Ab/C
ooh ooh
I want to follow your star wherever it leads me and I don't mind Lord, I hope you don't mind. I wanna walk with you and talk with you and

Am7
C/D
G
D/F♯
Bm7
B♭m7
D♭/E♭
A♭
E♭/G
Cm7
do all the things you want me to do 'cause I know that
Jesus
Je - sus is love. I
Em7
G7
C
G/B
Am7
C/D
Fm7
A♭7
D♭
A♭/C
B♭m7
D♭/E♭
know, and if you ask I'll
show love is the word for - ev - er.
G
D/F♯
Em
G7/D
A♭
E♭/G
Fm
A♭7/E♭
1. Who can bring you love? Je - sus!
Who can bring you joy? Je - sus!
Who can turn your life around? Je-sus! Oh, oh
2. Call Him in the morning!
Call Him in the evening!
Call Him in the midnight hour!
C
G/B
Am7
D♭
A♭/C
B♭m7
Repeat and fade
yeah yeah yeah yeah yeah yeah yeah!

LADY
(December 10, 1980)

Words and Music by
Lionel Richie

* Recorded 1/2 step higher, in E♭ minor

Gm/D C/D Dm
To Coda
hold you in my arms for - ev - er more. You have
hear you whis - per soft - ly in my ear. In my
Gm7 Am7 D Bbmaj7 Am7
gone and made me such a fool, I'm so lost in your
mf
Dsus D Gm7 Am7 D7
love. And oh, we be - long to - geth - er,
Bbmaj7 Am7 Dsus D
D.S. al Coda
Won't you be - lieve in my song?

Coda
Gm7
Am7
D7
B♭maj7
Am7
eyes I see no one else but you, There's no oth - er love like
mf
Dsus
D
Gm7
Am7
D7
our love. And yes, oh yes, I'll al - ways want you near me,
B♭maj7
Am7
Dsus
D
B♭
3
I've wait - ed for you for so long. La - dy,
f
C/B♭
F
C/E
Dm
Dm/C
B♭
your love's the on - ly love I need, And be - side me

C/B♭ F C/E Dm Dm/C
is where I want you to be. 'Cause
B♭ C/B♭ F C/E
my love, there's some-thing I want you to
Dm Dm/C B♭ Gm7 C11
3fr.
know. You're the love of my life, you're my
Dm Gm/D C/D Dm
8va
La-dy.
mp
Slower

ENDLESS LOVE

(June 24, 1981)

Words and Music by
Lionel Richie

D/E E E/A A E/A
E♭/F F F/B♭ B♭ F/B♭
you're ev - 'ry step I take.
Oh, and and
Dmaj7 D/E E A E/G♯
E♭maj7 E♭/F F B♭ F/A
3
I I want to share all my
F♯m7 E6 Dmaj7 D/E E
Gm7 F6 E♭maj7 E♭/F F
love with you. No one else
A Em7/A Dmaj7 D/E E
B♭ Fm7/B♭ E♭maj7 E♭/F F
To Coda
3
will do, and your eyes, they tell me how

Amaj7 E/G♯ F♯m7 E6 Dmaj7 C♯m7
4fr.
B♭maj7 F/A Gm7 F6 E♭maj7 Dm7
much you care. Oh yes, you will al - ways be
Bm7 D/E Aadd2
Cm7 E♭/F B♭add2
3
my end - less love.
A
B♭
3
Two hearts, two hearts that
D D/E E E/A A
E♭ E♭/F F F/B♭ B♭
3
beat as one, our lives have just be - gun for -

D
E♭
- ev - er. I hold you close in my arms
D/E E E/A A E/A
E♭/F F F/B♭ B♭ F/B♭
I can't re - sist your charms, And
Dmaj7 D/E E A E/G♯
E♭maj7 E♭/F F B♭ F/A
love, I'd be a fool for
F♯m7 E6 Dmaj7 D/E E
Gm7 F6 E♭maj7 E♭/F F
you. I'm sure you know I don't

Amaj7
B♭maj7
Em7/A
Fm7/B♭
Dmaj7
E♭maj7
D/E
E♭/F
E
F
mind, 'cause you, you mean the
E/A
F/B♭
A
B♭
E/G♯
F/A
F♯m7
Gm7
E6
F6
Dmaj7
E♭maj7
C♯m7
4fr.
Dm7
world to me. Oh, I know I found in
Bm7
Cm7
D/E
E♭/F
A
B♭
D.S. al Coda
you my end - less love.
Coda
Em7/A
Fm7/B♭
Dmaj7
E♭maj7
D/E
E♭/F
E
F
And yes, you'll be the

E/A A E/G♯ F♯m7 Dmaj7 C♯m7
4fr.
F/B♭ B♭ F/A Gm7 E♭maj7 Dm7
on - ly one. Oh no, I can't de- ny this love
f
Dmaj7 C♯m7 Dmaj7 C♯m7
E♭maj7 Dm7 E♭maj7 Dm7
I have in - side, And I'll give it all to you, my
Bm7 D/E A
Cm7 E♭/F B♭
love, my end - less love.
dim.
p
3
D D/E E E/A A
E♭ E♭/F F F/B♭ B♭

OH NO
(September 4, 1981)

Words and Music by
Lionel Richie

Moderately slow, with expression (♩ = 86)

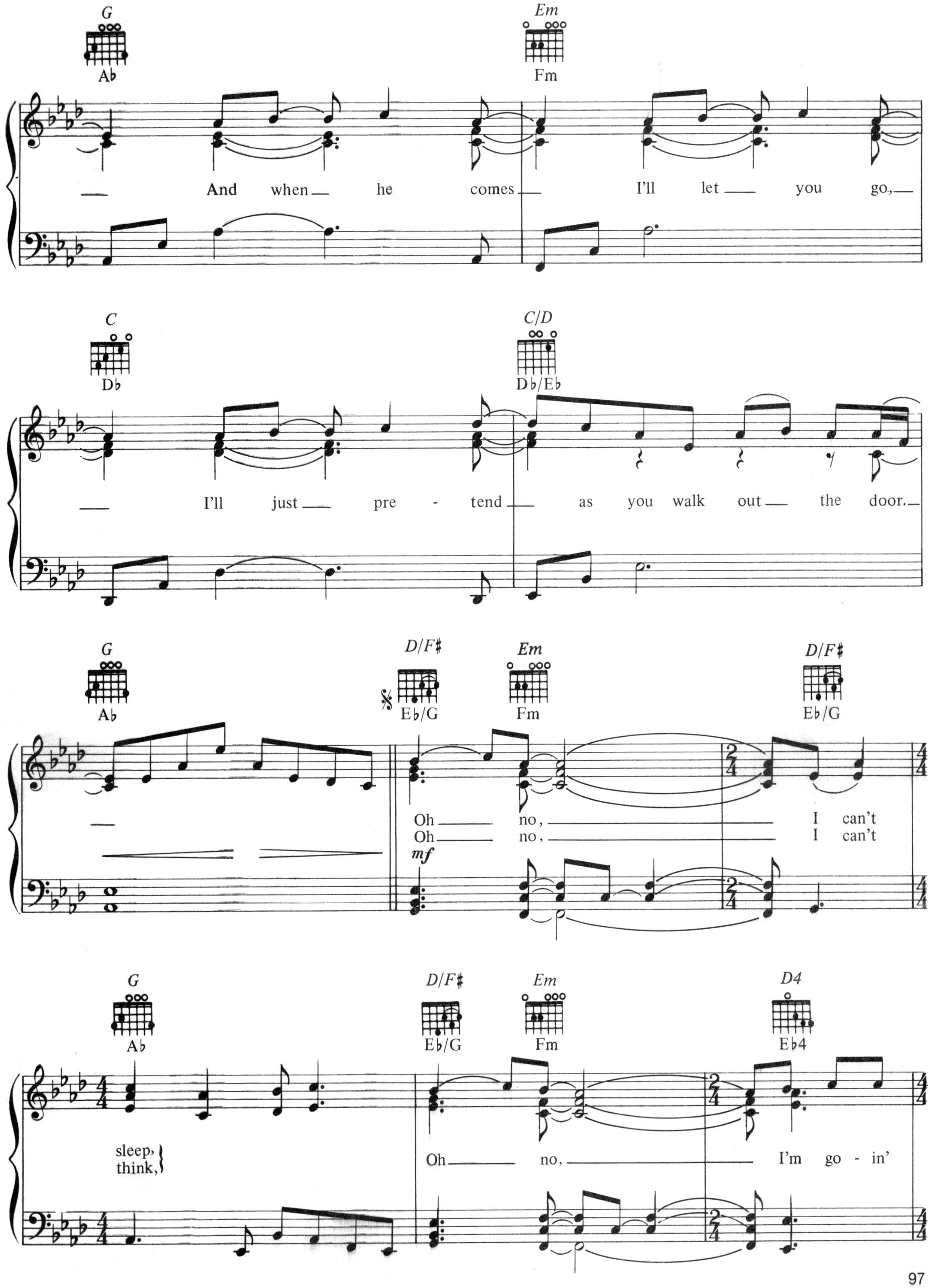
G
A♭
Em
Fm
And when he comes I'll let you go,
C
D♭
C/D
D♭/E♭
I'll just pre - tend as you walk out the door.
G
A♭
D/F♯
E♭/G
Em
Fm
D/F♯
E♭/G
Oh no, I can't
Oh no, I can't
mf
G
A♭
D/F♯
E♭/G
Em
Fm
D4
E♭4
sleep,
think,
Oh no, I'm go - in'

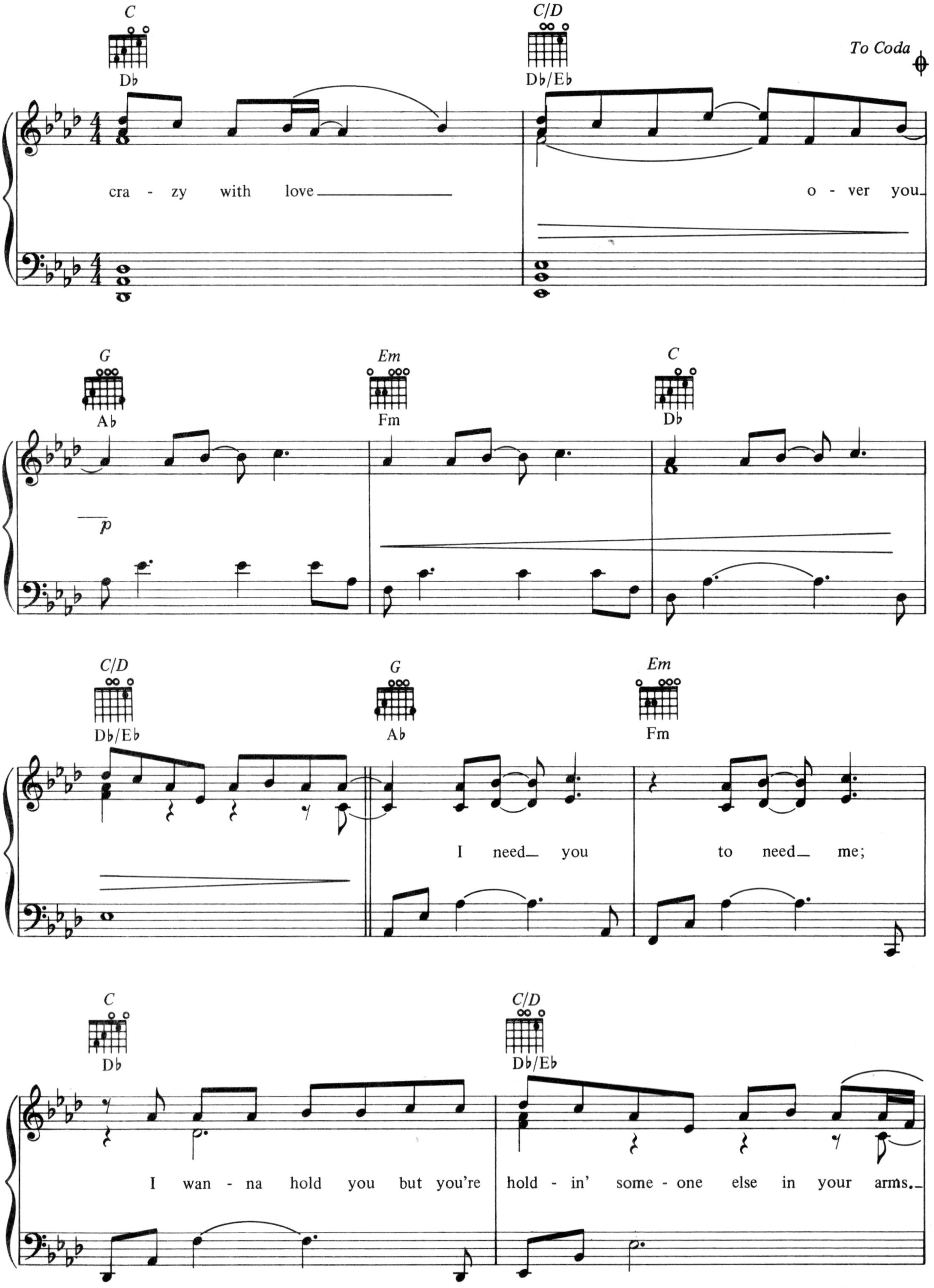
C
Db
C/D
Db/Eb
To Coda
crazy with love
over you
G
Ab
Em
Fm
C
Db
p
C/D
Db/Eb
G
Ab
Em
Fm
I need you to need me;
C
Db
C/D
Db/Eb
I wanna hold you but you're holdin' someone else in your arms.

G
Ab
When I close my eyes
Em
Fm
I see your face;
C
Db
I'm just not sure
C/D
Db/Eb
how much my heart can e - rase.
G
Ab
D.S. al Coda
Coda
G
Ab
Em
Fm
Oh, hon -
C
Db
ey,
C/D
Db/Eb
G
Ab

Em
Fm
C
D♭
oh, su - gar,
C/D
D♭/E♭
G
A♭
p
D/F♯
E♭/G
Em
Fm
D/F♯
E♭/G
G
A♭
Oh no, I can't sleep an - y - more, ba - by.
D/F♯
E♭/G
Em
Fm
D/F♯
E♭/G
G
A♭
Oh no, I can't think an - y - more, ba - by.

D/F♯ Em D4 C
E♭/G Fm E♭4 D♭
Oh no, I'm go - in' cra - zy with love
C/D G
D♭/E♭ A♭
o - ver you.
p
Em C
Fm D♭
C/D G
E♭/D♭ A♭
rit.
with more motion
rall.

LUCY
(Album date: June 22, 1981)

Words and Music by
Lionel Richie

Am7
D11
B♭m7
E♭11
while?
G
G/F
Em
E♭
3fr.
A♭
A♭/G♭
Fm
E
First saw you, Lu - cy, down in New Or - leans;
G
G/F
Em
E♭
3fr.
A♭
A♭/G♭
Fm
E
I was a drift - er, you were a Ca - jun queen.
G
G/F
Em
E♭
3fr.
A♭
A♭/G♭
Fm
E
You had man - y fel - las with lots of style and you drove 'em wild

Am7
B♭m7
D11
E♭11
'cause then I knew
oh, that Lu - cy I had to be
G
A♭
F
G♭
C/F
D♭/G♭
with you.
G
A♭
G
A♭
G/F
A♭/G♭
Em
Fm
E♭
3fr.
E
Trav - eled 'round the coun - try and I made my way,

G G/F Em Eb 3fr.
Ab Ab/Gb Fm E
but I nev - er once for - got what I felt that day.
G G/F Em Eb 3fr.
Ab Ab/Gb Fm E
Now I think I'm read - y to play my hand, I wan - na be your man I
Am7 D11
Bbm7 Eb11
know it's hard to do.
Oh Lu - cy, I'm so in love with
G F C/F G
Ab Gb Db/Gb Ab
you.

F Gb C/E Db/F
I've been a wan - d'rin' man for such a
G Ab F Gb C/E Db/F G Ab D/F# Eb/G G Ab D/F# Eb/G
long time, but now I know just where I'm go - in'.
F Gb C/E Db/F G Ab
Oh how I need ya, dear Lu - cy, by my side. Don't you go
F Gb Gadd9 Ab add9
a - way 'cause I'm so in love with you.

1. *Voice Tacet*
2. Been searching for ya, Lucy, for such a long time.
3. Now I wanna let you know just, what I have on my mind.
4. You know I been a man all alone; a lonely man,
   I been a lonely man, Lucy.
5. I don't wanna live my life without you.
6. *Voice Tacet*
7. There were times that I tried to get you off my mind, girl,
8. But, you're the girl of my dreams, Lucy,
9. Sometimes I find myself callin' your name out loud,
10. Lucy.
11. Oh, girl, I want you;
12. Oh, girl, I need you.

TRULY
(November 24, 1982)

Words and Music by
Lionel Richie

Fmaj7 Em7 Fmaj7 Em7
Gbmaj7 Fm7 Gbmaj7 Fm7
lov - er And I know if you real - ly care I will
near me And I feel with you in my arms This
1. 2.
Dm7 G7/4 G G4 G Dm7 G7/4 G G4 G
Ebm7 Ab7/4 Ab Ab4 Ab Ebm7 Ab7/4 Ab Ab4 Ab
al - ways be there love will last for - ev - er be - cause I'm
cresc.
C(2) C7 Fmaj7
Db(2) Db7 Gbmaj7
tru - ly, Tru - ly in love with you, Girl
F/G C(2) C7
Gb/Ab Db(2) Db7
I'm tru - ly, head o - ver

Fmaj7
Gbmaj7
F/G
Gb/Ab
C(2)
Db(2)
heels with your love I need you
C7
Db7
Fmaj7
Gbmaj7
F/G
Gb/Ab
And with your love I'm free
3
3
And
C(2)
Db(2)
C7
Db7
3
F
Gb
C/E
Db/F
Dm7
Ebm7
tru - ly,
You know you're all right
Dm7-5
Ebm7-5
C(2)
Db(2)
with
me

JUST PUT SOME LOVE IN YOUR HEART

(November 24, 1982)

Words and Music by
Lionel Richie

G4 G C
Ab4 Ab Db
world
And give the word
F(2) G4 G
Gb(2) Ab(4) Ab
hap - pi - ness To ev - 'ry boy and girl
G4 G Fmaj7 Em7
Ab4 Ab Gbmaj7 Fm7
Why can't we un - der - stand
Dm7 Dm7/G G Fmaj7
Ebm7 Ebm7/Ab Ab Gbmaj7
That the whole world wants to live?
With so man - y

Em7
Fm7
Dm7
Ebm7
reach - ing out
Is love so hard to give?
G4
Ab4
G
Ab
Dm7/G
Ebm7/Ab
G
Ab
C
Db
F(2)
Gb(2)
Just put some love in your
G4
Ab4
G
Ab
C(2)
Db(2)
heart.
rall.

YOU ARE
(December 28, 1982)

Words and Music by
Lionel Richie and Brenda Harvey-Richie

Moderately

G C G/C F/C C
Ab Db Ab/Db Gb/Db Db
And need - ing you so, My
And my love, you'll see, We'll
F/C G/C C Am7 G/A Am
Gb/Db Ab/Db Db Bbm7 Ab/Bb Bbm
love for you — I'll nev - er let go; I've got so —
stay to - geth - er, just you and me; I've got so —
Am/G F
Bbm/Ab Gb
— much love. — All I want — is to
— much love. — On - ly you —
G C F
Ab Db Gb
hold you, — Let me show — how much — I love you
(know me), — Tell me how — to love you

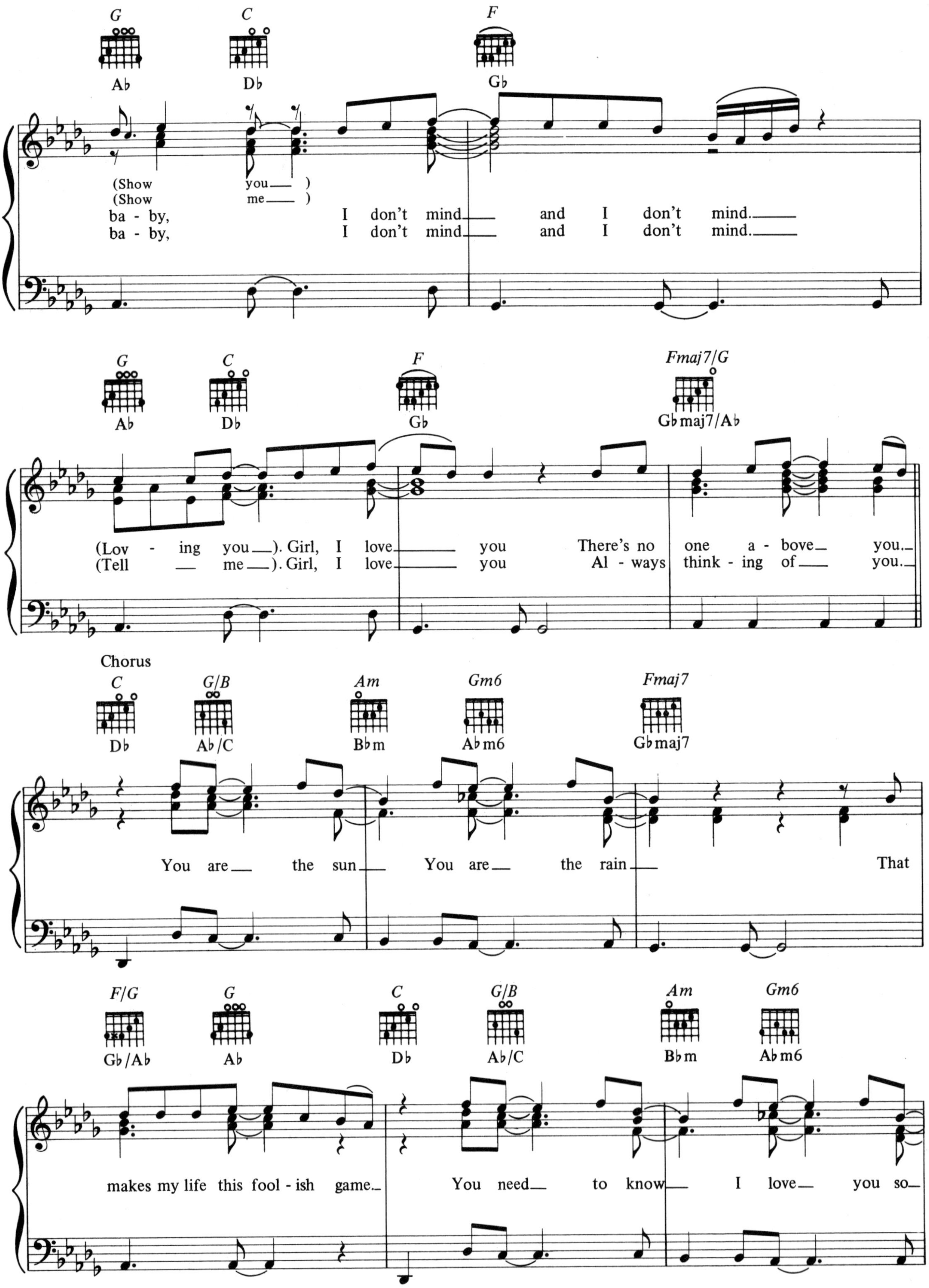
G C F
Ab Db Gb
(Show you)
(Show me)
ba - by, I don't mind and I don't mind.
ba - by, I don't mind and I don't mind.
G C F Fmaj7/G
Ab Db Gb Gbmaj7/Ab
(Lov - ing you). Girl, I love you There's no one a - bove you.
(Tell me). Girl, I love you Al - ways think - ing of you.
Chorus
C G/B Am Gm6 Fmaj7
Db Ab/C Bbm Abm6 Gbmaj7
You are the sun You are the rain That
F/G G C G/B Am Gm6
Gb/Ab Ab Db Ab/C Bbm Abm6
makes my life this fool - ish game. You need to know I love you so

Fmaj7 F/G G C Am
Gbmaj7 Gb/Ab Ab Db Bbm
And I'd do it all a-gain and a-gain Oh
F Dm7 Dm7/G
Gb Ebm7 Ebm7/Ab
wo wo yea yea yea
1. C Am G/A Am
Db Bbm Ab/Bb Bbm
yea.
C G/C C Am G/A Am
Db Ab/Db Db Bbm Ab/Bb Bbm

2. C
Db
yea.
Oh girl
N.C.
F G C F G Bb
Gb Ab Db Gb Ab Cb
I know you know the way I feel And I need your love for al-
Am F G C
Bbm Gb Ab Db
N.C.
ways. 'Cause when I'm with you I fall in love A-
F Fmaj7/G
Gb Gbmaj7/Ab
gain and a-gain and a-gain, ba-by.

C G/B Am Gm6 Fmaj7
Db Ab/C Bbm Abm6 Gbmaj7
You are the sun You are the rain That
F/G G C G/B Am Gm6
Gb/Ab Ab Db Ab/C Bbm Abm6
makes my life this fool-ish game. You need to know I love you so
Fmaj7 F/G G C Am
Gbmaj7 Gb/Ab Ab Db Bbm
And I'd do it all a-gain and a-gain. Oh
F Dm7 Fmaj7/G
Gb Ebm7 Gbmaj7/Ab
Repeat and fade
wo wo.

YOU MEAN MORE TO ME
(December 28, 1982)

Words and Music by
Lionel Richie

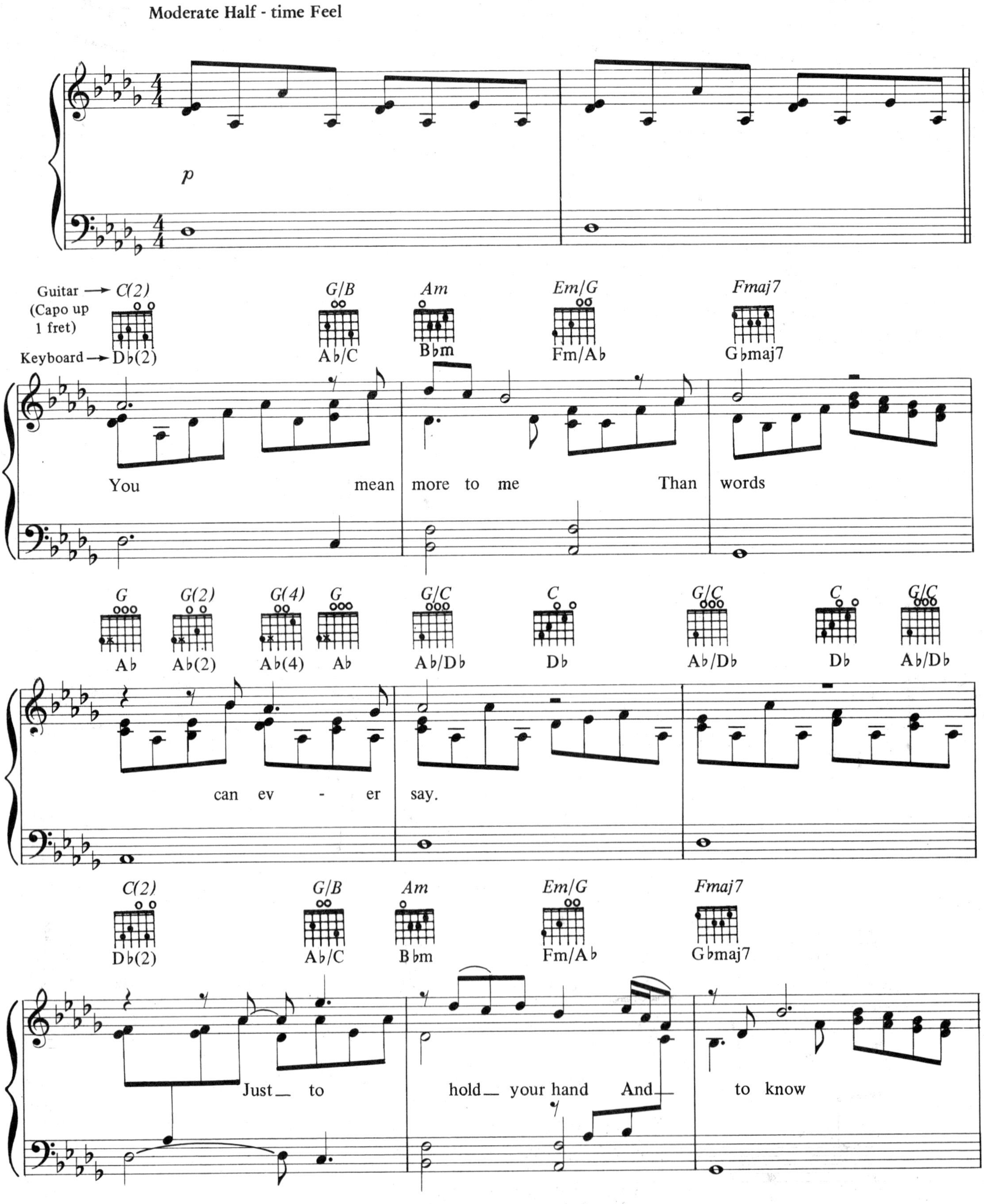

G(2) G(4) G Cmaj9 G/B Am Em/G
Ab(2) Ab(4) Ab Dbmaj9 Ab/C Bbm Fm/Ab
our love will stay; It feels so right_ (When) you're
Fmaj7 Em7 Dm7 F/G E7 E+ E7
Gbmaj7 Fm7 Ebm7 Gb/Ab F7 F+ F7
in my arms_ My love, to - night. Oh
rall.
C(2) G/B Am Em/G Fmaj7
Db(2) Ab/C Bbm Fm/Ab Gbmaj7
you, you mean more to me_ Than an - y love_
in tempo
G G(2) G(4) G G/C C G/C C G/C
Ab Ab(2) Ab(4) Ab Ab/Db Db Ab/Db Db Ab/Db
I've_ ev - er known._

C(2) G/B Am Em/G Fmaj7
D♭(2) A♭/C B♭m Fm/A♭ G♭maj7
And I want to give you all my love,
G(2) G(4) G Cmaj9 B♭/C
A♭(2) A♭(4) A♭ D♭maj9 C♭/D♭
Just you a - lone.
Fmaj7 Em7 B♭
G♭maj7 Fm7 C♭
You're all my dreams come true; There's so much
Fmaj7 Em7 Fmaj7 Em7
G♭maj7 Fm7 G♭maj7 Fm7
joy in your eyes And all the love you give,

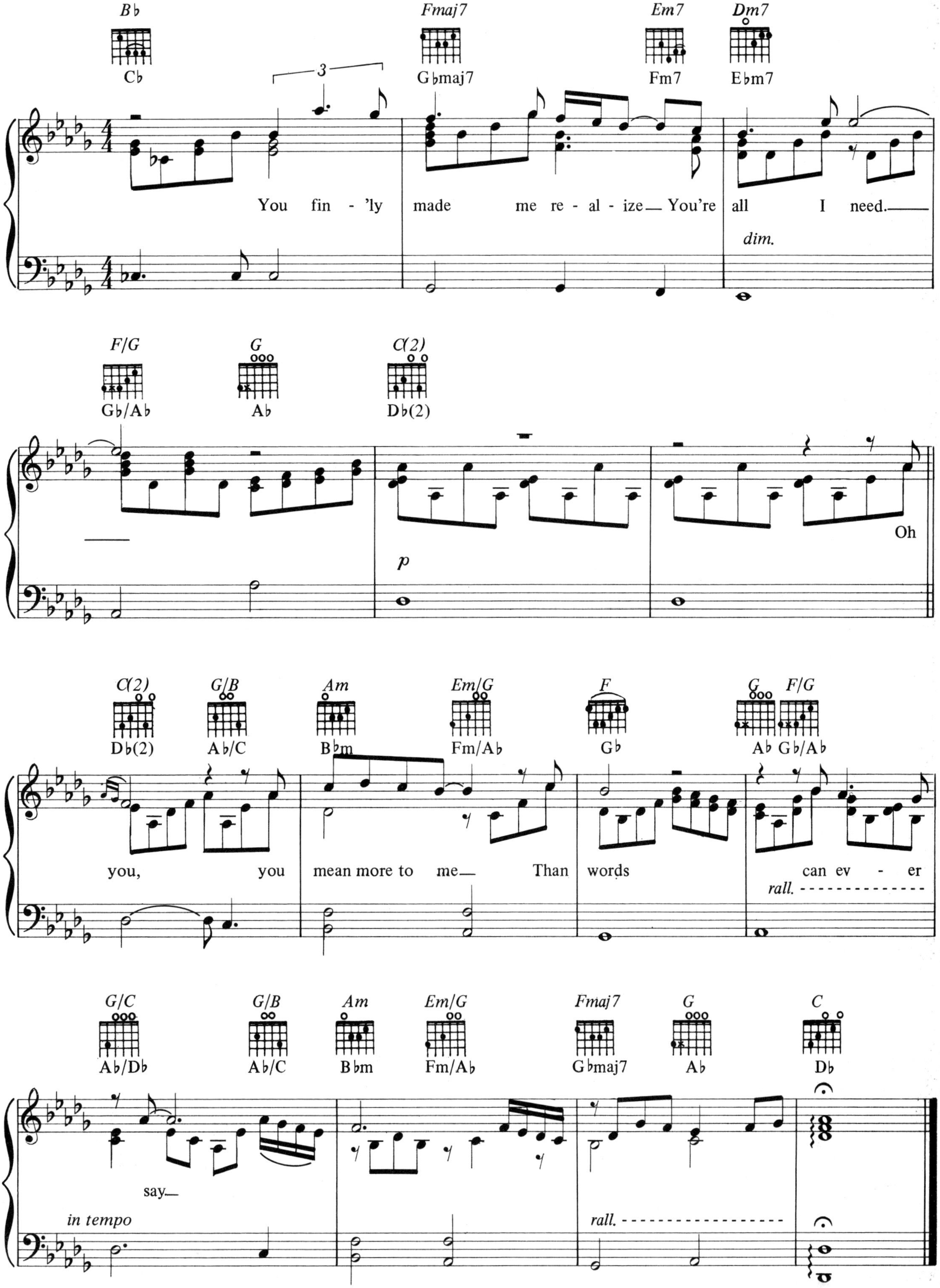
B♭ Fmaj7 Em7 Dm7
C♭ G♭maj7 Fm7 E♭m7
3
You fin - 'ly made me re - al - ize You're all I need.
dim.
F/G G C(2)
G♭/A♭ A♭ D♭(2)
p
Oh
C(2) G/B Am Em/G F G F/G
D♭(2) A♭/C B♭m Fm/A♭ G♭ A♭ G♭/A♭
you, you mean more to me Than words can ev - er
rall.
G/C G/B Am Em/G Fmaj7 G C
A♭/D♭ A♭/C B♭m Fm/A♭ G♭maj7 A♭ D♭
say
in tempo
rall.

MY LOVE
(March 25, 1983)

Words and Music by
Lionel Richie

C(2) C/D G(2)
Db(2) Db/Eb Ab(2)
But I sho' need you by my side. My love,
Chorus
G D/G C C/D
Ab Eb/Ab Db Db/Eb
f
just think - in' a - bout you ba - by Just
G D/G C(2) C/D
Ab Eb/Ab Db(2) Db/Eb
blows my mind. My love,
G D/G C C/D
Ab Eb/Ab Db Db/Eb
just think - in' a - bout you ba - by Just

G D/G C(2) C/D
A♭ E♭/A♭ D♭(2) D♭/E♭
blows my mind all the
G
A♭
time.
dim.
G 7fr. D6/F♯ 5fr. Em7 Bm/D
A♭ E♭6/G Fm7 Cm/E♭
p
Life with me I know for sure it ain't been eas - y,
C(2) C/D G(2)
D♭(2) D♭/E♭ A♭(2)
But you stayed with me an - y - way.

G D6/F♯ Em7
7fr.
5fr.
A♭ E♭6/G Fm7
3
And e - ven though you ain't gon - na lose too much by leav - ing,
C(2) C/D G
7fr.
D♭(2) D♭/E♭ A♭
I'm so glad you stayed.
My love,
G D/G C C/D G D/G
A♭ E♭/A♭ D♭ D♭/E♭ A♭ E♭/A♭
just think - in' a - bout you ba - by Just blows my mind.
C(2) C/D G D/G C C/D
D♭(2) D♭/E♭ A♭ E♭/A♭ D♭ D♭/E♭
My love, just think - in' a - bout you ba - by Just

G D/G C(2) C/D To Coda G
Ab Eb/Ab Db(2) Db/Eb Ab
blows my mind. all the time.
p cresc.
C C/D G
Db Db/Eb Ab
You've been my friend and you've been my lov - er, oh Lawd
f
C C/D G
Db Db/Eb Ab
Hon - ey, you're ev - 'ry - thing I need.
C C/D G Bm/F♯ Bø7/F
Db Db/Eb Ab Cm/G Cø7/Gb
You've made my love so strong, now I know where I be - long.

E7
Am7
Bm7
Cmaj7
3fr.
F7
B♭m7
Cm7
D♭maj7
3
Oh girl, you'll nev - er have to wor - ry
Oh
Cmaj7/D
7fr.
G(2)
Dm/G
D♭maj7/E♭
A♭(2)
E♭m/A♭
ba - by, an - y - more, an - y -
C(2)
Cm(2)
D♭(2)
D♭m(2)
D.S. al Coda
more
My love,
f sub.
Coda
G
D/G
C(2)
C/D
G
A♭
E♭/A♭
D♭(2)
D♭/E♭
A♭
time
Oh
yeah
rall.

WANDERING STRANGER
(August 31, 1983)

Words and Music by
Lionel Richie

Tenderly (with a half time feel)

p
Am G F
I am a Wan - 'dring Stran - ger, Lost and all a - lone;
Some- times I'm lone - ly, But I can - not fool my - self;
smoothly
R.H.
C G/B Am G4 G
I am a mil - lion miles a - way,
I must keep mov - ing till I find

F
Am
me.
Oh
I know you're wait-
I know I'm hurt-
G4
G
F
C
G/B
ing for me To come home a-gain,
ing you, But try to un-der-stand,
Am
G4
G
F
But I am search-ing for an an-swer.
My piece of mind is all I'm af-ter.
G/F
Fmaj7
G/F
Please try to un-der-
Help me if you

Am(2)
stand
can
1. And
2.
Fmaj7
G/C
Fmaj7
G/C
I love you
And you love me,
Fmaj7
G/C
F(2)
G(2)/F
Some - day we can make it
to - geth - er.
Fmaj7
G/F
Am(2)
G
Just you and me

F(2)
Am
G
Just you and me
F
Am(2)
1.
2.
rall.
rall.
F
Am
G
in tempo
Oh my love
in tempo
F
Am
G
I do love

*Guitar solo omitted

F
Am
G(2)
F
Can you help me make it through?
Try to re-
Am
G(2)
F
mem - ber
Wom - an, I
Am
G(2)
N.C.
F
love you.
ff
Am
G

N.C.
F
Am
G
con 8
F
Am
G
Dm
Am
Em
Bm
F♯m
C♯m
4fr.
D/E
Calmly and much slower
N.C.
p

SERVES YOU RIGHT
(November 10, 1983)

Words and Music by Lionel Richie,
Greg Phillinganes and John Maclain

E
F
Am7
Bbm7
think - in'_ of __
did - n't_ care,_
There was so much
And I was beg - ging
mag - ic in your_
ba - by, please don't_
Fmaj7
Gbmaj7
Dm7
Ebm7
F/G
Gb/Ab
Am7
Bbm7
__ eyes.
__ go.
Then one day you said
Now you're cry-ing, tell-ing me
G/A
Ab/Bb
Am7
Bbm7
Dm7
Ebm7
E
F
we_ were through
what_ went wrong
You said you found some - bod - y_ new,_
Girl, you stayed a - way too_ long,_
Am7
Bbm7
G/A
Ab/Bb
Am7
Bbm7
Fmaj7
Gbmaj7
And then you turned and you walked right_ out the door._
Can't you see I've__ got you_ off my mind._

Dm7 F/G Bb/C C7
Ebm7 Gb/Ab Cb/Db Db7
Ba - by, I told you his love was - n't true
Think - in' 'bout the 2.3. pain that you put me through,
Fmaj7 D7/4 D7 Fmaj7/G
Gbmaj7 Eb7/4 Eb7 Gbmaj7/Ab
N.C.
You did - n't hear me, so now I say these words to you:
I can't help you be - cause it feels good tell - ing you:
Chorus
Dm9 Fmaj7 Em7 Am7
Ebm9 Gbmaj7 Fm7 Bbm7
Serves you right for say - in' good - bye
Now you say you're sor - ry.
Dm9 Fmaj7 Em7 Am7
Ebm9 Gbmaj7 Fm7 Bbm7
Serves you right for say - in' good - bye,
ba - by

Rap No. 1

"See mama, what I'm tryin' to say
to you is that, I'm, you know, I love
ya, but ya - ya hurt me so bad, I
can't take it no more girl, I just
can't take it, No . . . Hell No."

"No! No, No, I don't wanna hear it,
don't say it anymore, don't talk
no more, I'm tired of you're lyin',
I'm tired of your cryin' girl, tell
me . . . don't tell me."

N.C.
(Back round for Rap No. 1)
R.H.
Both hands 8va lower
1.
2.
Dm7
F/G
D.S. al Coda
E♭m7
G♭/A♭
Think-in' 'bout the
as is
Coda
Dm7/B♭
Gm7
Dm9
Fmaj7
E♭m7/C♭
A♭m7
E♭m9
G♭maj7
Oh ___ yeah.
Serves you right_ for say-in' good-bye_

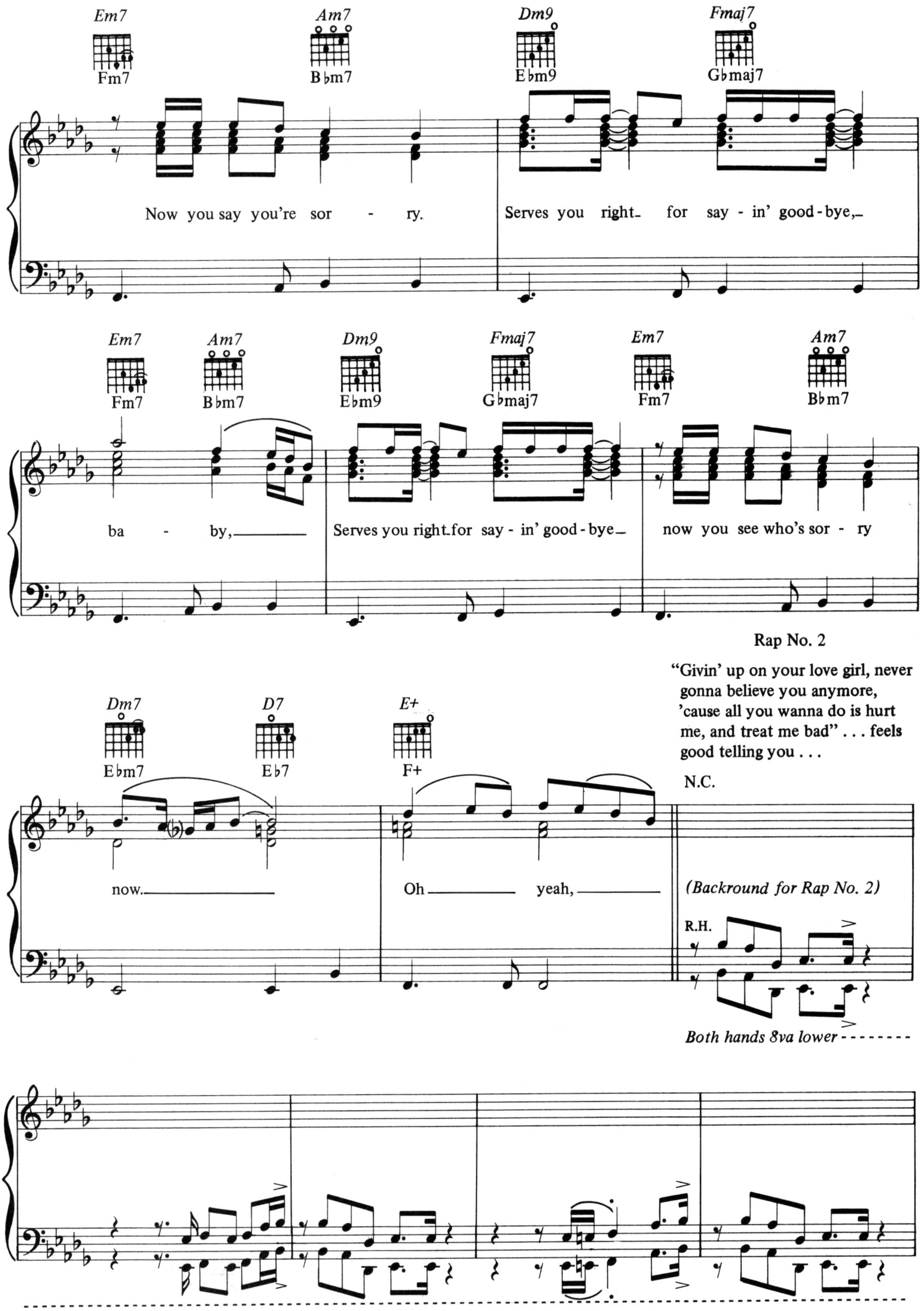
Em7 Am7 Dm9 Fmaj7
Fm7 B♭m7 E♭m9 G♭maj7
Now you say you're sor - ry.
Serves you right for say - in' good - bye,
Em7 Am7 Dm9 Fmaj7 Em7 Am7
Fm7 B♭m7 E♭m9 G♭maj7 Fm7 B♭m7
ba - by,
Serves you right for say - in' good - bye
now you see who's sor - ry
Rap No. 2
"Givin' up on your love girl, never gonna believe you anymore, 'cause all you wanna do is hurt me, and treat me bad" . . . feels good telling you . . .
Dm7 D7 E+
E♭m7 E♭7 F+
N.C.
now.
Oh yeah,
(Backround for Rap No. 2)
R.H.
Both hands 8va lower

Dm9 F/G
Ebm9 Gb/Ab
feel good tell-in' you:
Dm9 Fmaj7 Em7 Am7
Ebm9 Gbmaj7 Fm7 Bbm7
Serves you right for say-in' good-bye
Girl, I just don't need you
(Ad lib) Don't say you're sor-ry, baby
Serves you right for say-in' good-bye All you do is use my love,
Serves you right for say-in' good-bye 'Cause your words don't mean a thing,
Serves you right for say-in' good-bye,
Can't let you hurt me an-y-
It's you who's sor-ry
Dm7 D7 Dm7/Bb Gm7
Ebm7 Eb7 Ebm7/Cb Abm7
Repeat and fade
more,
now,
Oh Oh.

ALL NIGHT LONG (ALL NIGHT)

(August 31, 1983)

Words and Music by
Lionel Richie

Moderate Caribbean feel (♩ = about 104)

(Drums)
mf
(Synth.)
(Voice)
Da da
Oh
Guitar (Capo up 1 fret)
G
F
Am
5fr.
Piano
Ab
Gb
Bbm
Well, my friends, the time has come raise the roof and
Peo - ple danc - ing all in the street, see the rhy - thm all

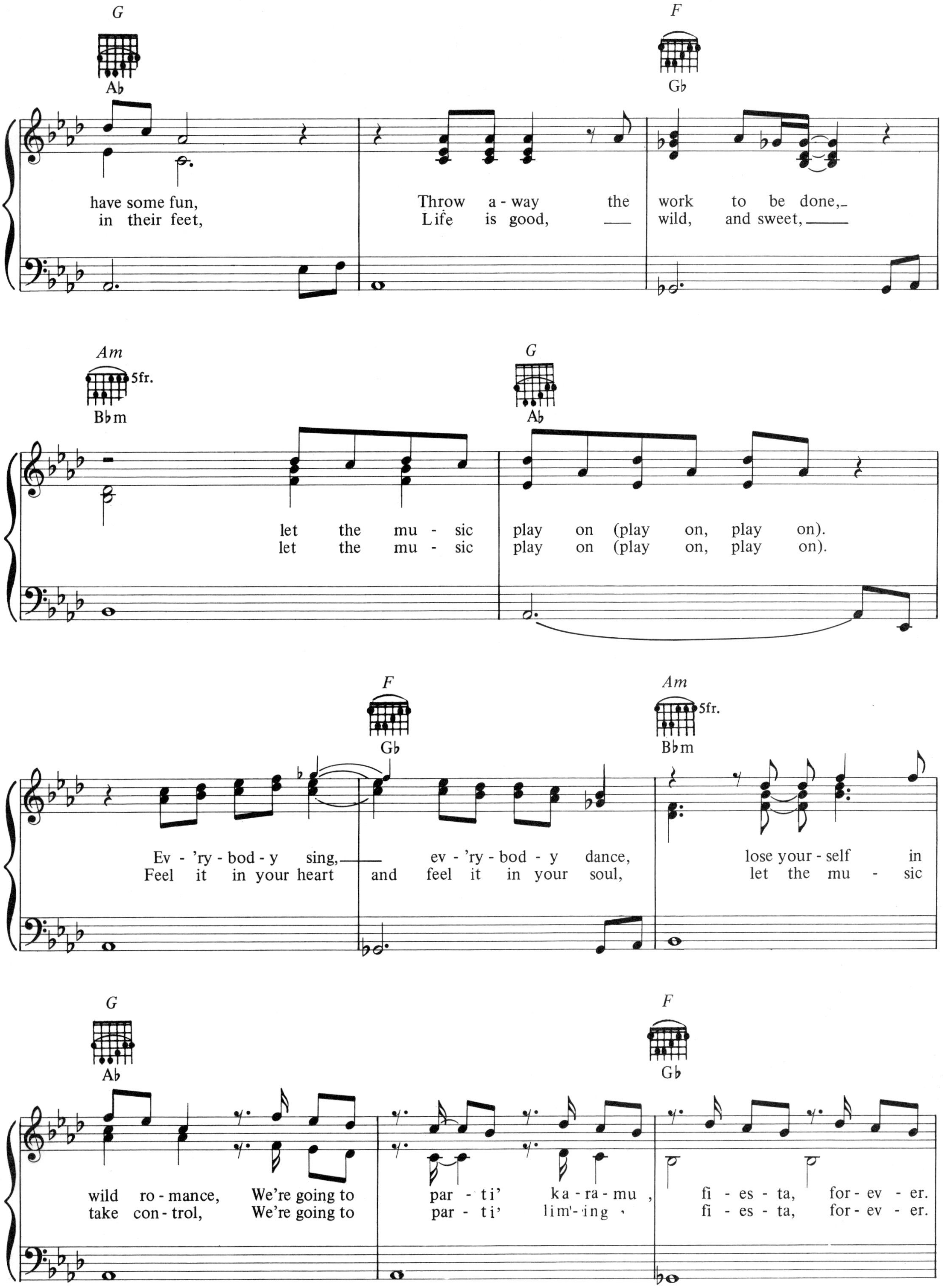
G
A♭
F
G♭
have some fun, Throw a-way the work to be done,
in their feet, Life is good, wild, and sweet,
Am
5fr.
B♭m
G
A♭
let the mu-sic play on (play on, play on).
let the mu-sic play on (play on, play on).
F
G♭
Am
5fr.
B♭m
Ev-'ry-bod-y sing, ev-'ry-bod-y dance, lose your-self in
Feel it in your heart and feel it in your soul, let the mu-sic
G
A♭
F
G♭
wild ro-mance, We're going to par-ti' ka-ra-mu, fi-es-ta, for-ev-er.
take con-trol, We're going to par-ti' lim'-ing fi-es-ta, for-ev-er.

2nd time omit these bars
Am
5fr.
B♭m
G
A♭
Come on and sing a - long: We're going to par - ti' ka - ra - mu, fi - es - ta, for - ev - er.
Come on and sing a - long: We're going to par - ti' lim - ing, fi - es - ta, for - ev - er.
F
G♭
Am
5fr.
B♭m
Come on and sing a - long:
Come on and sing my song:
G
A♭
Chorus
G
A♭
F
G♭
All night long, (All night) all night, All night
G
A♭
F
G♭
long, (All night) all night, All night long, all night,

1. G
A♭
All night long, Oh.
2. G
A♭
(All night) long, (All night) Yeah!
N.C.
F
G♭
Once you get start - ed you can't sit down,
N.C.
F
G♭
Come join the fun, it's a mer - ry - go - round,

F
G♭
N.C.
Ev - 'ry - one's danc - ing their trou - bles a - way,
N.C.
Fmaj7 Em7 Fmaj7 Em7
G♭maj7 Fm7 G♭maj7 Fm7
Come join our par - ty, see how we play!
N.C.
Fmaj7 Em7 Fmaj7 Em7
G♭maj7 Fm7 G♭maj7 Fm7
N.C.
N.C.
Tom bo li de say de moi ya
Yeah, Jam - bo Jum - bo

Way to par - ti' o we goin'
Oh, jam - ba - li.
Tom bo li de say de moi ya
Yeah, Jam - bo Jum - bo.
Fmaj7 Em7 Fmaj7 Em7 G11
G♭maj7 Fm7 G♭maj7 Fm7 A♭11
Oh
Fmaj7 Em7 G
G♭maj7 Fm7 A♭
3
Yes We're gon - na have a par - ty All night

F
G♭
long, (All night) all night, All night
G
A♭
long, (All night) all night, All night
F
G♭
long, all night, All night
G
A♭
long (All night) (All night)

F
G♭
Ev - 'ry - one you meet, they're jam - ming in the street, All night
G
A♭
long. (All night) (yeah, I said) (feel good, feel good) (All night)
F
G♭
G
A♭
Repeat and fade
(All night) (yeah, I said) (feel good, feel good) (All night)

RUNNING WITH THE NIGHT

(November 10, 1983)

Words and Music by
Lionel Richie and Cynthia Weil

Strong Steady 4 (♩ = 122)

Am
F
G
The heart of the cit - y street was beat - ing;
Am
Light from the ne -
F
G
ons turned the dark to day.
Am
F
We were too hot to think of sleep-

G
Am
ing;
We had to get out
F
G
Am
3
be - fore the mag - ic got a - way
We were run -
Am
G/A
Am
ning with the night,
Play -
G/A
Am
ing in the sha - dows
Just

G/A
F
G/F
F
you and I
'til the morn-ing light.
G/F
F
G/F
F
G/F
F
G/F
F
G/F
Pianists: Omit vocal melody
To Coda
(We were run-ning) Oh
(run-ning with the
Am
F
night). You were look-ing so good girl, heads were turn-
G
Am
ing.
You and me on the town

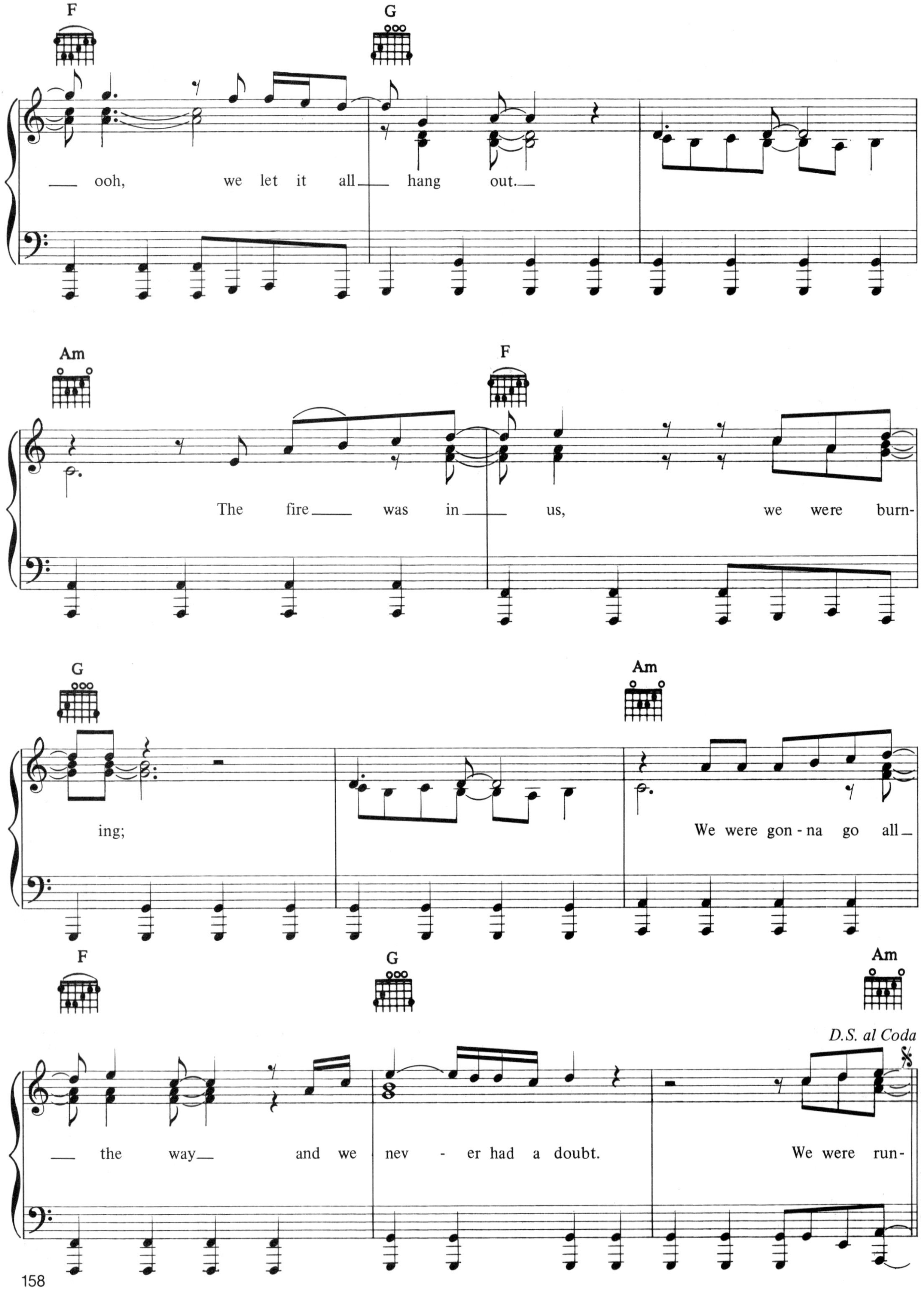
F
G
— ooh, we let it all — hang out. —
Am
F
The fire — was in — us, we were burn-
G
Am
ing;
We were gon - na go all —
F
G
Am
D.S. al Coda
— the way — and we nev - er had a doubt.
We were run-

Coda
Am G/A Am G/A Am G/A Am G/A Am G/A F
night) (backround for guitar solo)
Am G/A Am G/A Am G/A Am G/A Am G/A F
B♭ F C
We were so in love you
G B♭ F C
and me On the boul - e - vard wild

G
B♭
F
C
and free.
Giv - ing all we got, we laid
G
B♭
F
C
it down,
Tak - ing ev - 'ry shot we took
G
Am
the town.
We were run-
G/A
Am
G/A
ning with the night,
Play - ing in the sha - dows

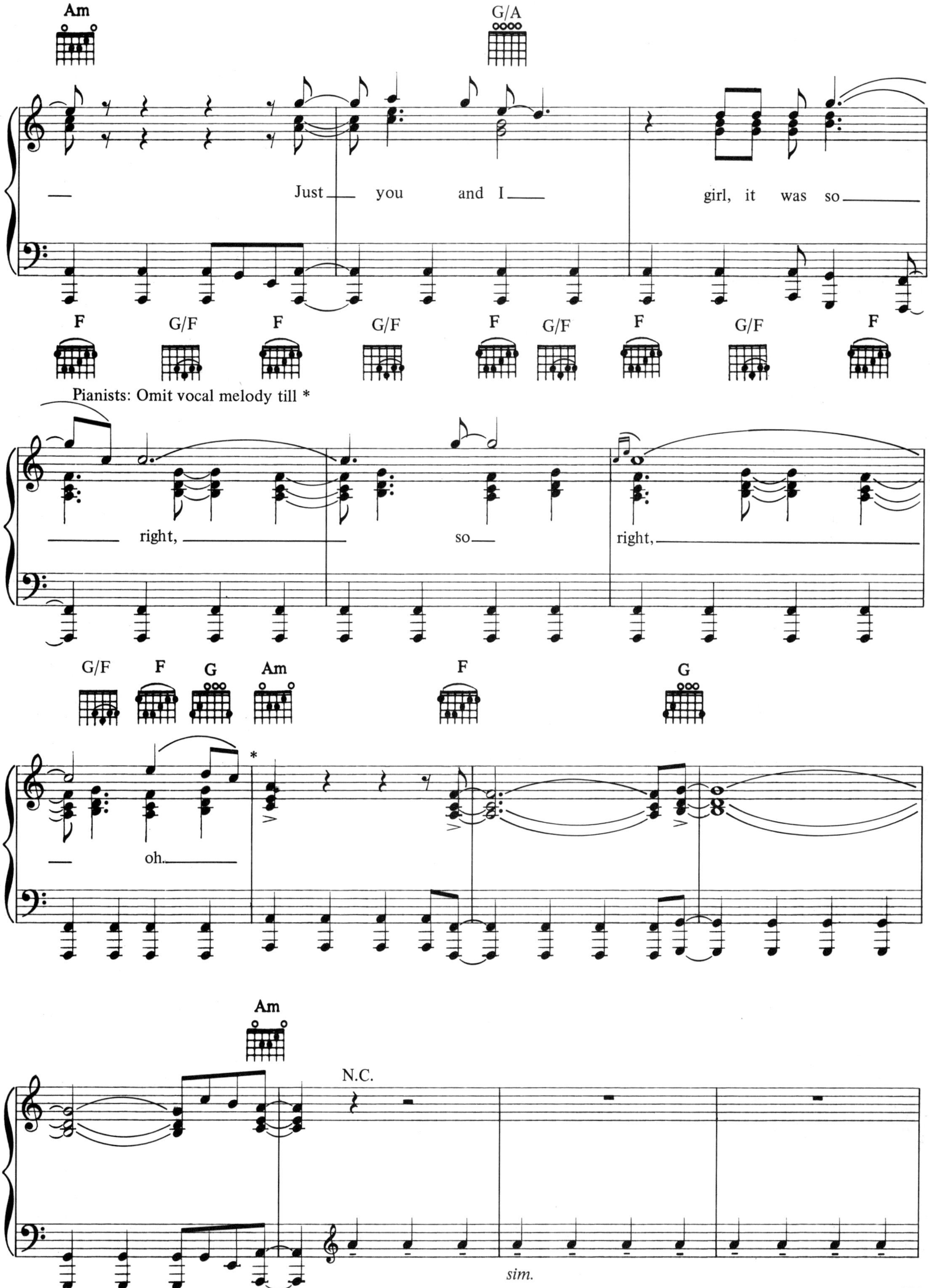
Am
G/A
Just you and I girl, it was so
F
G/F
Pianists: Omit vocal melody till *
right, so right, oh.
G
N.C.
sim.

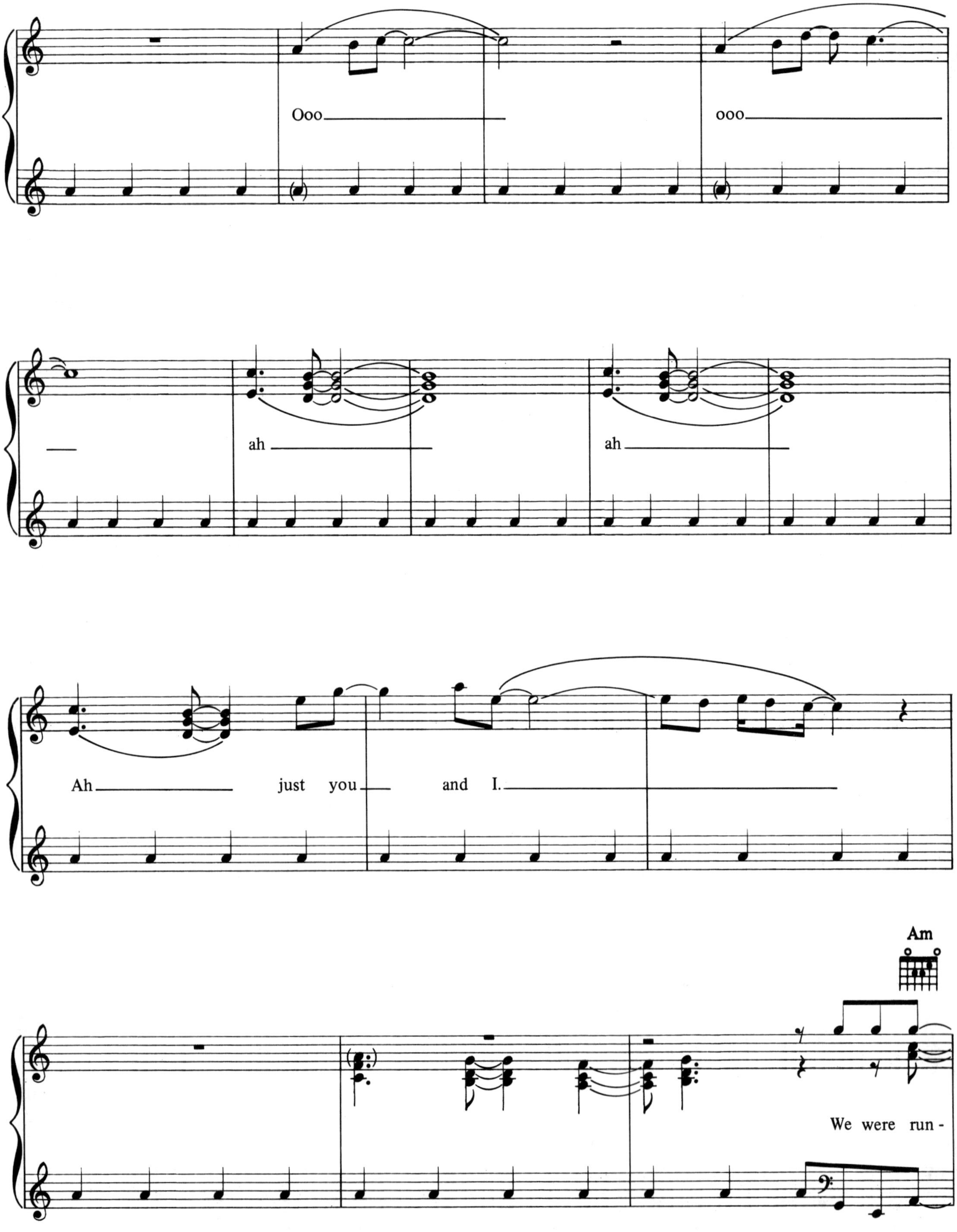
Ooo
ooo
ah
ah
Ah
just you
and I.
Am
We were run -

* Final guitar solo omitted

HELLO
(February 14, 1984)

Words and Music by
Lionel Richie

Slow ballad (♩ = 62)
mp
I've
Am
G6
Fmaj7
G6
Fmaj7
1. been a - lone with you in - side my mind And
2. long to see the sun - light in your hair And
3. Instrumental
Am
G6
Fmaj7
G6
Fmaj7
in my dreams I've kissed your lips a thou - sand times. I
tell you time and time a - gain how much I care. Some-

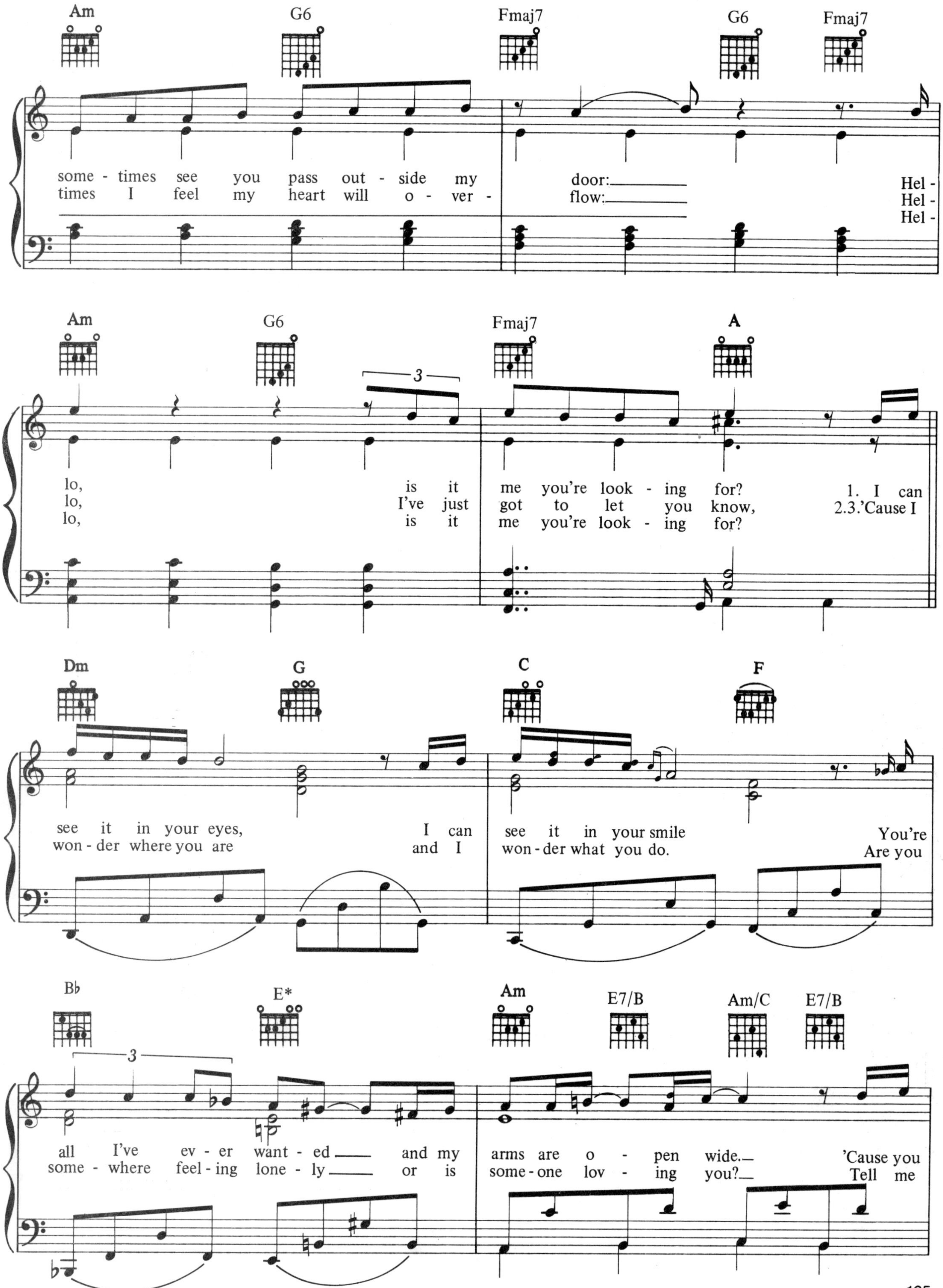

* Recorded version has G♯ in bass.

Dm G C F
3
know just what to say and you know just what to do And I
how to win your heart for I have - n't got a clue But
B♭ Am/E E
1.2.
Am G6 Fmaj7 G6 Fmaj7
a tempo
want to tell you so much, I love you . . .
let me start by say - ing, I love you . . .
Am G6 Fmaj7 G6 Fmaj7
2. I
3. Inst.
3.
Am G6 Fmaj7 G F A
you.
rall. . . . .

STUCK ON YOU
(June 11, 1984)

Words and Music by
Lionel Richie

Moderate Country 4 (♩ = 134)
mp smoothly
F
Am
B♭
1.3. Stuck on you I've got this feel- in' down deep in my soul
2. Stuck on you Been a fool too long I guess it's

F
Am
— that I just — can't — lose: —
time for — me to come on home. —
Guess I'm on — my — way.
Guess I'm on — my — way.
Bb
C
F
Need - ed a friend —
So hard to see —
Am
Bb
C
And the way I feel now I guess I'll — be with you — till the end.
That a wom - an like you could wait a - round for a man — like — me.
F
Am
Bb
To Coda
Guess I'm on — my — way, —
Guess I'm on — my — way, —

C
F
Am
Might - y glad you stayed.
Might - y glad you stayed.
Bb
C
F
Am
Bb
C
Bb
C
F
F/E
Oh, I'm leav - ing on that mid - night train to - mor-
mf
more rhythmically

Dm
Bb
C
- row
And I know just where I'm go-
F
Bb
- - - in',
I've packed up my trou-
C
F
F/E
Dm
bles and I've thrown them all a-way.
C
Dm
C
Dm
'Cause

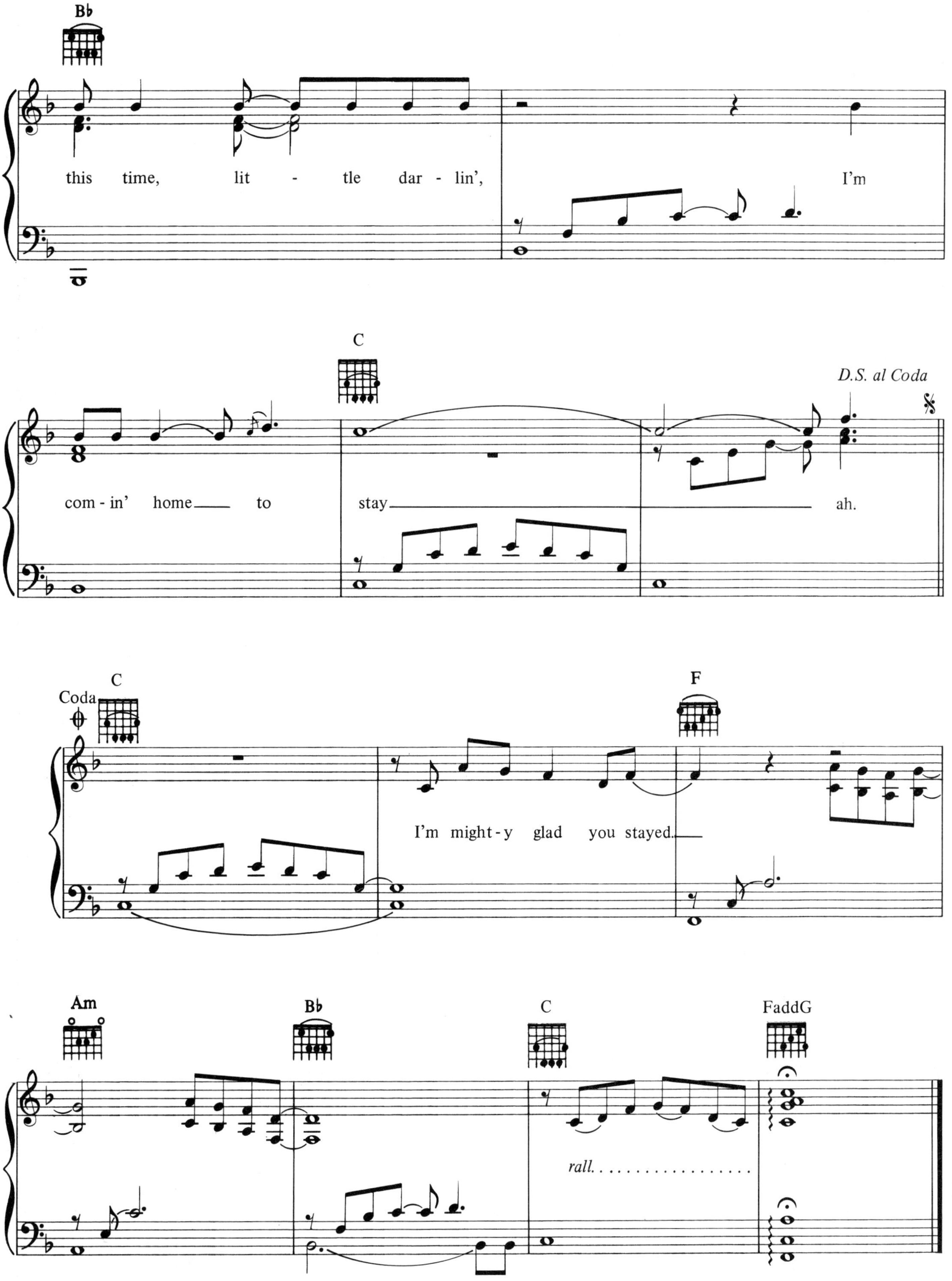
B♭
this time, lit - tle dar - lin', I'm
C
D.S. al Coda
com - in' home to stay ah.
Coda
C
F
I'm might - y glad you stayed.
Am
B♭
C
FaddG
rall.

CAN'T SLOW DOWN
(Album date: October 14, 1983)

Words and Music by
Lionel Richie and David Cochrane

Moderate funk 4 (♩= 124)

Cm
Bb/C
I know what's on your mind you feel you're wast - ing time,
I'm out here on the run, try - ing to get things done.
Ab/Eb
Gm7
Cm
Wan - na talk a - bout it? You feel there's some - thing wrong
Can you hear me ba - by? You think my love's no - where
Bb/C
Ab/Eb
don't feel like hold - ing on, You bet - ter
you think I just don't care, Are you
Gm7
Cm
think a - bout it. You say you just can't see,
kid - ding ba - by? Don't make me play no games.

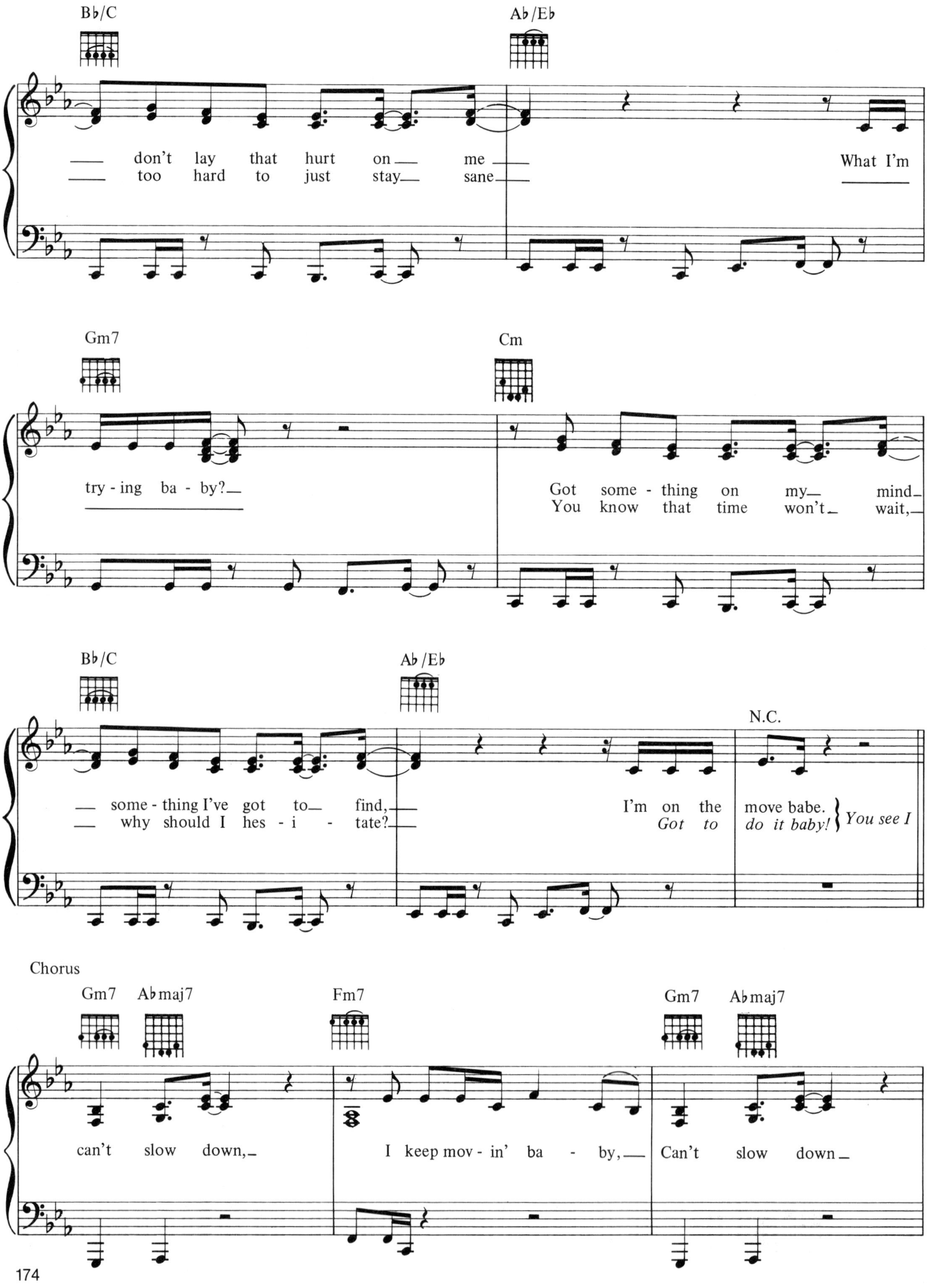
Bb/C
Ab/Eb
don't lay that hurt on me
too hard to just stay sane
What I'm
Gm7
Cm
try-ing ba-by?
Got some-thing on my mind
You know that time won't wait,
Bb/C
Ab/Eb
N.C.
some-thing I've got to find,
why should I hes-i-tate?
I'm on the move babe.
Got to do it baby!
You see I
Chorus
Gm7
Abmaj7
Fm7
Gm7
Abmaj7
can't slow down,
I keep mov-in' ba-by,
Can't slow down

Fm7
Gm7
Abmaj7
Fm7
No, I can't slow down,
Gm7
Abmaj7
Fm7
Cm
Can't slow down, got to keep mov - in' on.
Bb/C
Ab/Eb
Gm7
Cm
Bb/C
Ab/Eb
1.
N.C.
2.
Gm7

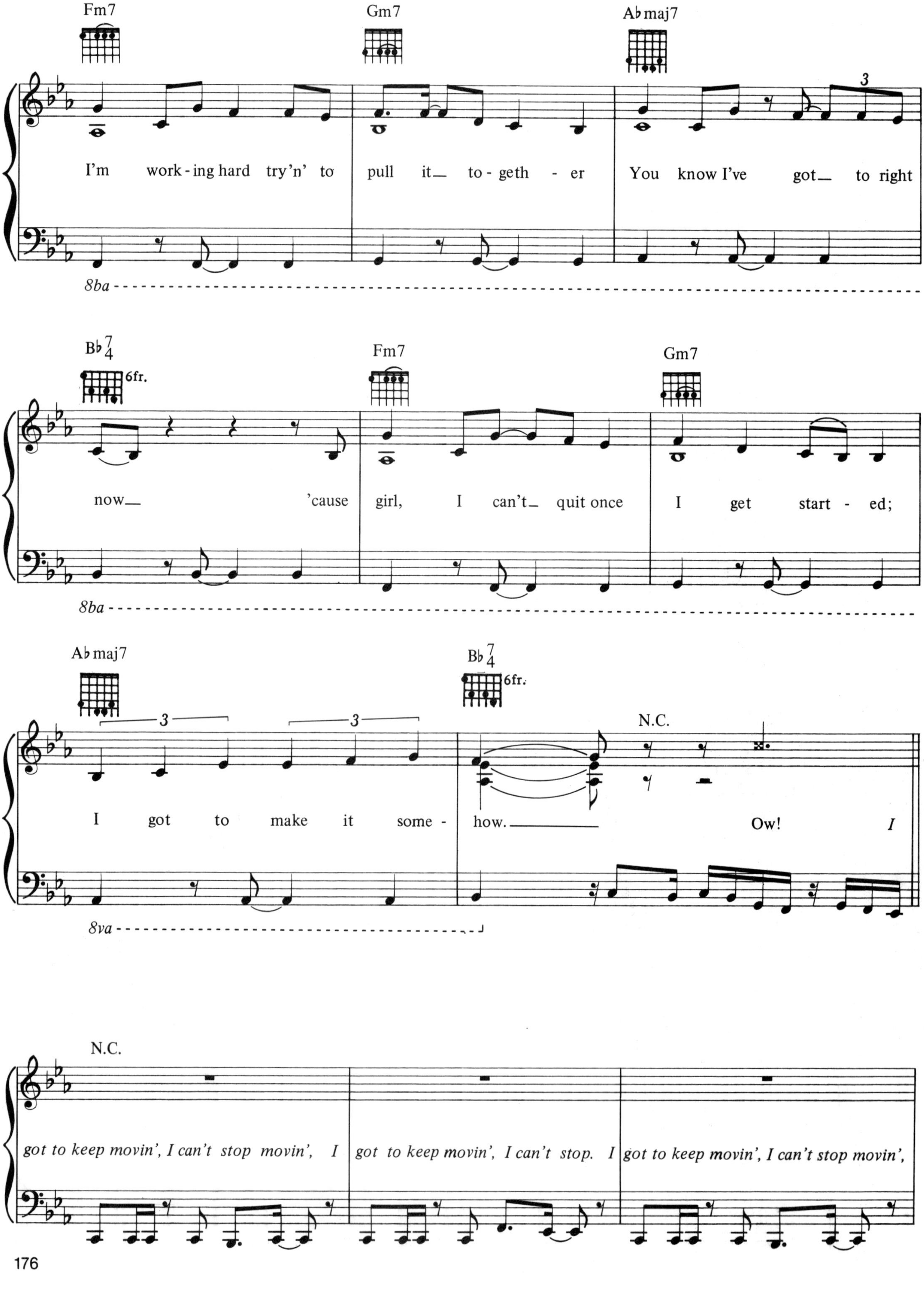
Fm7
Gm7
A♭maj7
I'm working hard try'n' to pull it to-geth-er You know I've got to right now 'cause girl, I can't quit once I get start-ed;
8ba
B♭7/4
6fr.
Fm7
Gm7
A♭maj7
B♭7/4
6fr.
N.C.
I got to make it some-how. Ow! I
8va
N.C.
got to keep movin', I can't stop movin', I got to keep movin', I can't stop. I got to keep movin', I can't stop movin',

N.C.
I got to keep movin', I can't stop. I got to keep movin', I can't stop movin', I got to keep movin', I can't stop.
I got to keep movin', I can't stop movin', I got to keep movin', I can't stop.
Gm7
Ab maj7
Can't slow down,
Fm7
Gm7
Ab maj7
Can't slow down,
Fm7
Gm7
Ab maj7
Can't slow down,
Fm7
Gm7
Ab maj7
Can't slow down,
Baby,

Fm7
Cm
B♭
Cm
B♭
Cm
Ooh girl, I'm all fired up I
B♭/C
A♭/E♭
just can't get e - nough, girl, of it.
Gm7
Cm
Ah girl, I'm on the one got to

Bb/C
Ab/Eb
N.C.
keep on keep-in' on,
oh yeah,
Oh, you see I
Gm7
Abmaj7
Fm7
3
can't slow down,
got to keep mov - in', ba - by,
Gm7
Abmaj7
Fm7
Can't slow down,
No, I
Gm7
Abmaj7
Fm7
Repeat and fade
can't slow down,
ad libs

THE ONLY ONE
(Album date: October 14, 1983)

Words and Music by
Lionel Richie and David Foster

Slow steady 2 (𝅗𝅥 = 66)

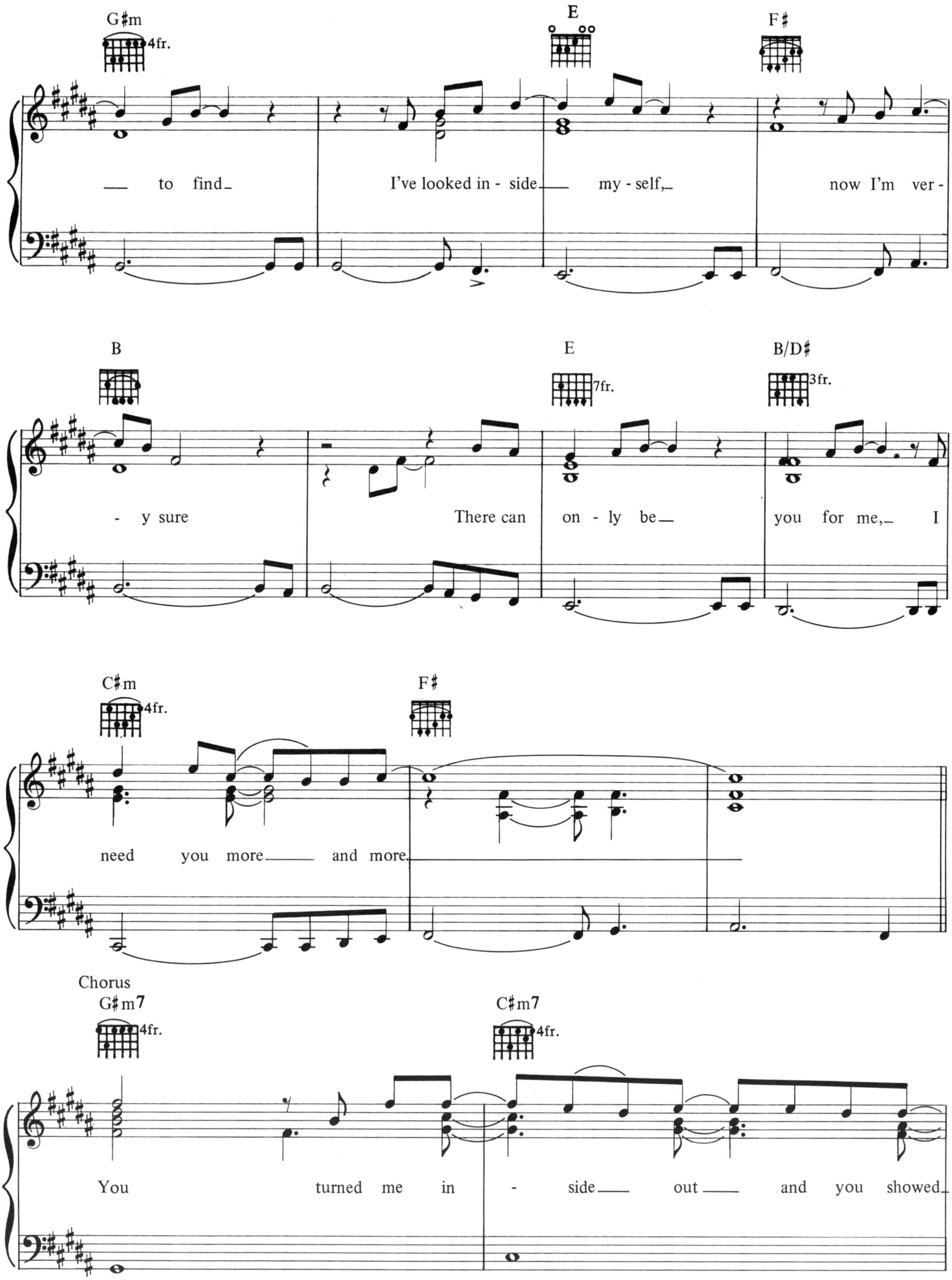
G♯m
4fr.
E
F♯
to find
I've looked in - side
my - self,
now I'm ver -
B
E
7fr.
B/D♯
3fr.
- y sure
There can
on - ly be
you for me,
I
C♯m
4fr.
F♯
need you more and more.
Chorus
G♯m7
4fr.
C♯m7
4fr.
You turned me in - side out and you showed

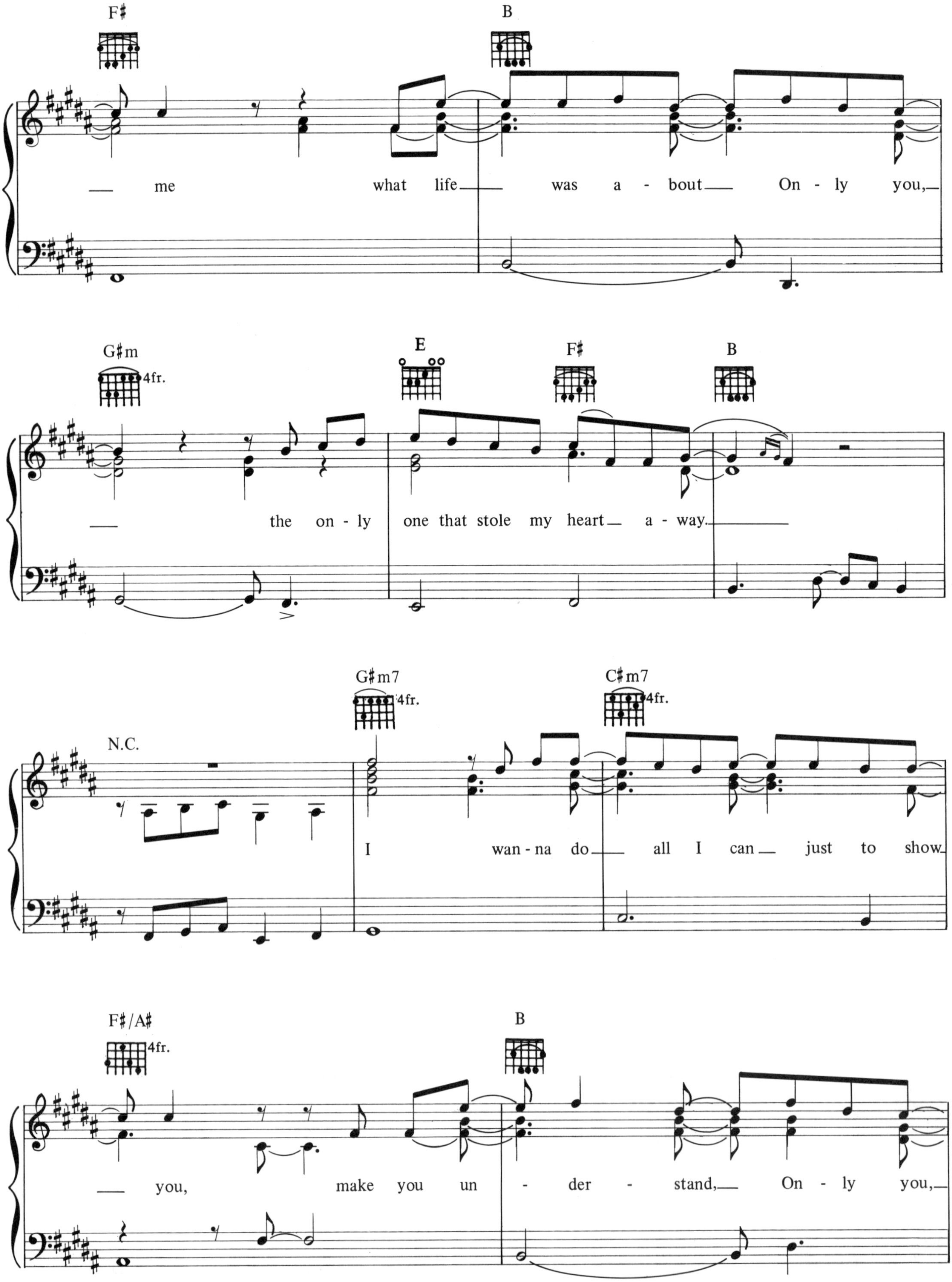
F♯ B
me what life was a - bout On - ly you,
G♯m 4fr. E F♯ B
the on - ly one that stole my heart a - way.
N.C. G♯m7 4fr. C♯m7 4fr.
I wan - na do all I can just to show
F♯/A♯ 4fr. B
you, make you un - der - stand, On - ly you,

G♯m
4fr.
E
F♯
the on - ly one that stole my heart a - way.
B
C♯m
4fr.
When you're in my arms,
F♯
B
when I'm close to you
B♯o
C♯m
4fr.
E/F♯
D♯/F𝄪
There's a mag - ic in your touch that just comes

G♯m
4fr.
E
F♯
— shin - ing through. Want you ev - 'ry day, want you ev -
B
E
7fr.
B/D♯
3fr.
- 'ry night, there can on - ly be you for me, you
C♯m
4fr.
F♯
make it seem so right. Oh girl, 'cause
G♯m7
4fr.
C♯m7
4fr.
You turned me in - side out and you showed

F♯
B
G♯m
4fr.
me what life was a - bout. On - ly you, the on - ly
E
F♯
B
N.C.
one that stole my heart a - way.
Fm7
B♭m7
E♭/G
A♭
4fr.
Fm7
D♭
4fr.
E♭
6fr.
3

Ab
4fr.
N.C.
Fm7
Bbm7
Eb/G
Ab
4fr.
Fm7
Db
4fr.
3
Eb
6fr.
Ab
4fr.
In my
Bbm
Eb/G
Ab
4fr.
mind, there's no oth - er love

Bbm
C7/E
You're the on - 'ly girl my heart and soul is
Fm
Db
4fr.
think - ing of
On - ly you,
Eb/Db
Cm7
Fm7
on - ly me,
there can nev -
Bbm
Cm7
er ev - er be an - oth - er
that

D♭
4fr.
D♭/E♭
un - der - stands the way that I feel in - side. 'Cause
Am7
Dm7
you turned me in - side out and you showed
G/B
C
Am7
me what life was a - bout. On - ly you, the on - ly
1.
Dm7
G
C
N.C.
one that stole my heart a - way. Yeah

2.
F G C
one that stole my heart a - way.
Am7 Dm7 G7/B
You, you stole my heart a - way (You stole it), You stole my
F/C C Am
heart a - way, on - ly you The on - ly
F G C
Repeat and fade
N.C.
one that stole my heart a - way. Yeah

PENNY LOVER
(September 17, 1984)

Words and Music by
Lionel Richie and Brenda Harvey-Richie

Moderate slow 4 (♩ = 98)

p
(2 bar percussion omitted)
Ab
4fr.
Fm
lightly
Pen - ny lov - er, don't walk on by,
Pen - ny lov - er, don't you make me cry.
Ab
4fr.
Can't you see girl, who my heart's beat - ing for?
Fm
You're the on - ly girl that I a - dore.

Ab
4fr.
Fm
Bbm
6fr.
Ab
4
fr.
3
The first time I saw you Oh, you looked
Gb
Ab
4fr.
Fm
so fine And I had a feel - in'
Bbm
6fr.
Ab
4fr.
Gb
Db/Gb
Gb
One day you'd be mine Hon - ey,
Ab
4fr.
Cm7
Fm
you came a - long and cap - tured my heart
2
4

Eb/F
Fm
Bbm
6fr.
Now my love is some-where lost in your
Db
4fr.
Eb
6fr.
Bbm
6fr.
kiss When I'm all a - lone it's you that
Db
4fr.
Eb
6fr.
Bbm
6fr.
I miss Girl, a love like yours is hard to re -
Db
4fr.
Eb
6fr.
Ab
4fr.
sist Oh

A♭
4fr.
Pen - ny lov - er, my love's on fire
Fm
Pen - ny lov - er, you're my one de - sire
A♭
4fr.
Tell me ba - by, could this be true
Fm
That I could need some - one like I need you

Ab
4fr.
Fm
Bbm
6fr.
Ab
4 fr.
3
Nights_ warm and ten - der Oh,_ ly - ing next
Gb
Ab
4fr.
Fm
_ to you Girl,_ I sur - ren - der
Bbm
6fr.
Ab
Gb
Db/Gb
Gb
what more_ can_ I_ do? I've spent
Ab
4fr.
Cm7
Fm
all of my life_ in search of your love_

Eb/F Fm Bbm 6fr.
Now there's one more thing I'd like to
Db 4fr. Eb 6fr. Bbm 6fr.
say Don't you ev - er take your sweet love a -
Db 4fr. Eb 6fr. Bbm 6fr.
way Girl, I'll do an - y - thing, just please
Db 4fr. Eb 6fr. Ab 4fr.
stay, Oh

Db 4fr.
Db/Eb 6fr.
Ab 4fr.
I don't un - der - stand it, Oh, what's come o - ver me
N.C.
Db 4fr.
Db/Eb 6fr.
But I'm not gon - na wor - ry, no not an - y -
Ab 4fr.
N.C.
Fm
Eb/F
more 'Cause when a man's in love he's on -
Fm
Eb/F
Fm
- ly got one sto - ry That's why my

B♭m 6fr.
D♭ 4fr.
E♭ 6fr.
3
love is some - where lost in your kiss When I'm lost
B♭m 6fr.
D♭ 4fr.
E♭ 6fr.
B♭m 6fr.
and a - lone it's you that I miss With a love like yours, it's hard
D♭ 4fr.
E♭ 6fr.
A♭ 4fr.
to re - sist, oh oh
A♭ 4fr.
Pen - ny lov - er, don't walk on by (Don't you walk on

Fm
by) Pen - ny lov - er, don't you make me cry (Don't you make me cry ba -
Ab
4fr.
by) Pen - ny lov - er, don't walk on by (Don't you walk on
Fm
by) Pen - ny lov - er, don't you make me cry (Oh Pen - ny
Ab
4fr.
Pen - ny lov - er, don't you walk on by (Don't you walk on by
ba - by)

Fm
Ab 4fr.
I remember the first time I saw you baby Pen - ny lov - er, don't you
Fm
make me cry— You had that look in your eye, you had that look in your eye, yeah yeah
Ab 4fr.
Fm
Ooh pretty baby, I just wanted to reach out and touch you baby, I wanted to reach out hold ya
Ab 4fr.
Fm
Repeat and fade
I wanted to reach out and say ooh ooh
I want to talk about you every day (Penny lover) Need you, just
Don't make me cry
need you, baby . . .

LOVE WILL FIND A WAY
(Album date: October 14, 1983)

Words and Music by
Lionel Richie and Greg Phillinganes

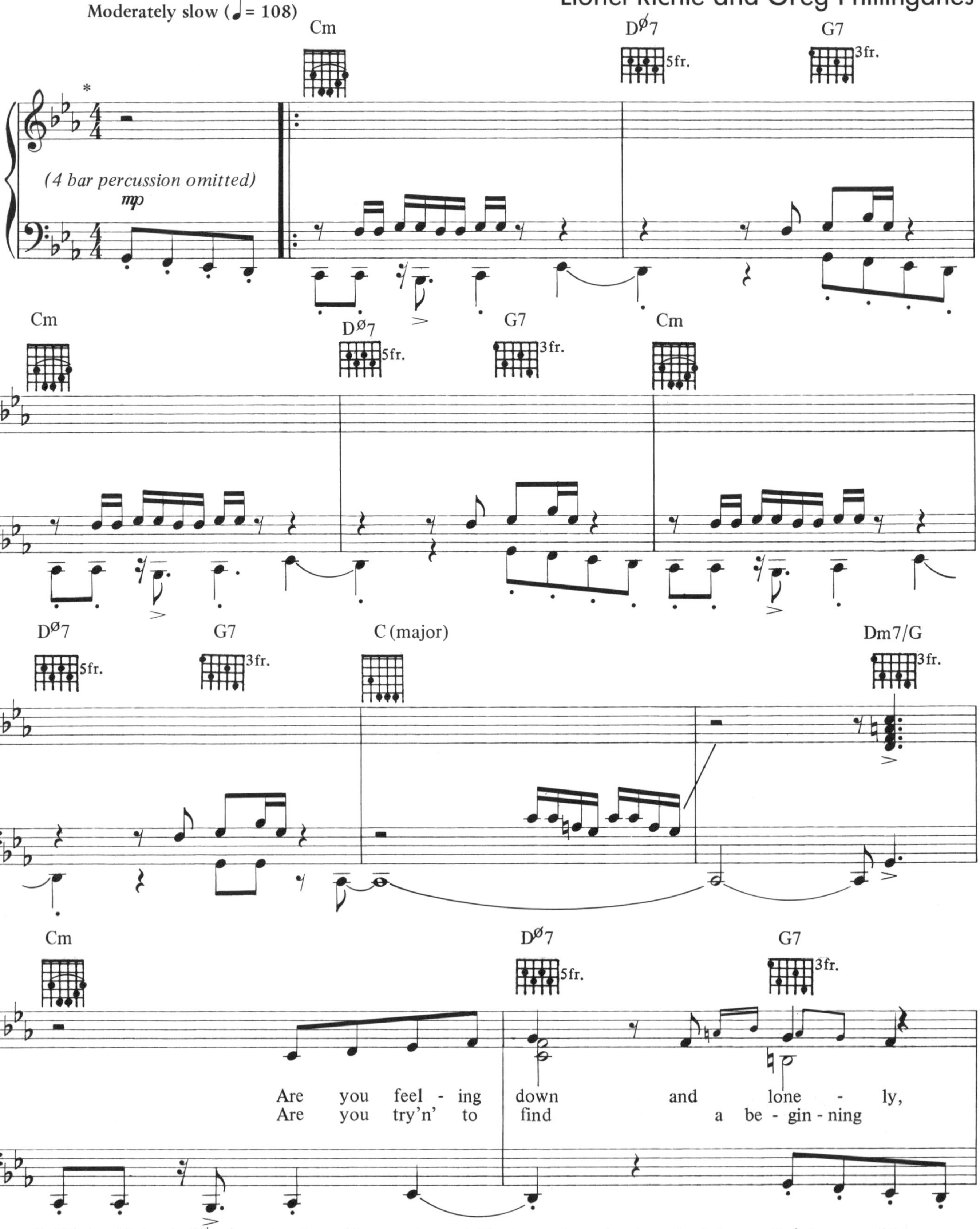

* Recorded ½ step higher in C♯ minor; to play with record, mentally change key signature to 4 sharps (♮'s become ♯'s). When modulation occurs, new key signature is 7 sharps.

Cm
D∅7 5fr.
G7 3fr.
feel - ing like you can't go on?
or some - thing just to hold on to?
sim.
Cm
D∅7 5fr.
G7 3fr.
C(maj.)
Just re - mem - ber love will find a way.
Al - ways know that love will find a way.
Dm7/G 3fr.
Cm
D∅7 5fr.
G7 3fr.
Tell me are you go - ing through chang - es,
Is it hard this life you're liv - ing?
Cm
D∅7 5fr.
G7 3fr.
Cm
time seems like it's pass - ing by?
Does the world seem so un - kind?
Just be - lieve that
Don't you wor - ry,

Dø7
5fr.
G7
3fr.
C
3
love will find a way.
love will find a way.
I see the
Some say we've
C
Cm7
tears you cry, I see the pain that's in your eyes;
lost our way, Some say the world has gone a - stray;
D7+5
G/B
Em
So man - y times you were so lone - ly and
But if you know where you're go - ing, there's
Cm7
D7
G7 4
C
no one seemed to care, But if your hopes for your to -
noth - ing you can't do, 'cause prob - lems will come and they will

D/C
7fr.
B∅7
E7
mor - rows are drown - ing in your sor - rows Know your heart
leave you The world will try to de - ceive you, But the truth
Am
1.
Am7/D
Dm7/G
3fr.
will show you the way.
will al -
2.
Am7/D
Dm7/G
3fr.
- ways be in your soul.
(Solo)
Cm
D∅7
5fr.
G7
3fr.
Cm
D∅7
5fr.
G7
3fr.

Cm
D∅7
5fr.
G7
3fr.
C
Do you want
Cm
D∅7
5fr.
G7
3fr.
Cm
some joy in your time? Are you try'n' to find some
- ing for a place to go where truth is all you'll
D∅7
5fr.
G7
3fr.
Cm
D∅7
5fr.
G7
3fr.
A♭
4 fr.
peace of mind? All you need to know is love will find a way.
ev - er know? All you need to say is love will find a way.
8ba
Fm7
D∅7
5fr.
N.C.
Repeat and fade
ooo
ooo
Are you look -
Do you want
8ba

The Closing Ceremonies at the 1984 Olympics in Los Angeles, California.

CONTENTS